Praise for *Transcer*

"For me, and most of my close colleagues, therapy is the fundamental psychotherapeutic approach that we use to help most of our adult patients who deal with the legacy of trauma. It is therefore a gift to all of us that Frank Anderson has written such a lucid, engaging, and comprehensive book that can help us navigate the complicated journey of resolving relational trauma. With the help of exquisite personal anecdotes, Anderson explains the deeper origins of apparently irrational and self-destructive behaviors that people have developed to deal with overwhelming realities. Most of all, he describes how to guide people in reclaiming "self-leadership" and taking back ownership of their lives. This is a wonderful book that should be read by anyone who wants to lay down the burdens of past trauma and those who seek to accompany them on this journey."

— **Bessel van der Kolk, MD,** President, Trauma Research Foundation Professor of psychiatry, Boston University School of Medicine author of *New York Times* bestseller *The Body Keeps the Score*

"A crucial contribution that brings clarity and light to the often dark, confusing journey of treating complex PTSD."

— **Richard C. Schwartz, PhD,** founder of Internal Family Systems (IFS)

"With his deeply compassionate attitude, Frank Anderson masterfully combines his years of clinical wisdom with the insights of neuroscience to create a definitive work on the treatment of complex trauma with IFS. This is a book that can and should be read by all therapists who work with trauma."

— **Janina Fisher, PhD,** author of *Transforming the Living Legacy of Trauma*

"In *Transcending Trauma*, Frank Anderson offers a methodical, clear, and highly instructive pathway to healing complex trauma through IFS, an astute therapeutic approach that is logically presented and generously illustrated with case examples and enriched by personal insights."

— **Gabor Maté, MD,** author of *When the Body Says No: Exploring the Stress-Disease Connection*

TRANSCENDING TRAUMA

Healing Complex PTSD with
Internal Family Systems Therapy

Frank G. Anderson, MD

Published by
PESI Publishing
3839 White Ave
Eau Claire, WI 54703
Cover: Amy Rubenzer
Editing: Jenessa Jackson, PhD, and Erik J. Martin
Layout: Amy Rubenzer & Bookmasters
ISBN: 9781683733973
Printed in the United States of America

PESI Publishing
pesipublishing.com

About the Author

Frank Anderson began his professional journey as a chemistry major at the University of Illinois in the pre-pharmacy program. He quickly developed a fascination with the workings of the human body and switched into a pre-medicine program. He happily entered Rush University Medical College, initially wanting to become a pediatrician due to his love of children, but switched into psychiatry after a close family member developed significant mental health symptoms. He was deeply touched by this experience and also keenly aware of the impact it had on others. During his  residency program in psychiatry at Harvard Medical School, he noticed that many of the clients struggling with major mental illness had also experienced significant trauma in their lives.

The pain he witnessed in others activated something deep within himself and compelled him to enter into therapy, which quickly connected him to his own trauma history. Becoming a psychiatrist at the Trauma Center in Boston under the direction of Bessel van der Kolk was a natural fit for him, where he learned more about trauma while simultaneously continuing his quest of helping others heal. He was fortunate enough to meet Dick Schwartz at a conference during this time, and his career focus instantly came into full alignment as he was able to integrate his knowledge of neuroscience and trauma treatment with Internal Family Systems (IFS) therapy.

Dr. Anderson is the former chair and executive director of the Foundation for Self Leadership, an organization focusing on IFS research and the expansion of the IFS model beyond psychotherapy. He authored the chapter "Who's Taking What? Connecting Neuroscience, Psychopharmacology and Internal Family Systems for Trauma" and coauthored the chapter "What IFS Brings to the Treatment of Trauma." He also coauthored the book *Internal Family Systems Skills Training Manual.*

He is a lead trainer and program consultant for the IFS Institute, is an advisor to the International Association of Trauma Professionals (IATP), and maintains a private practice. He is passionate about teaching and enjoys providing psychotherapy consultations, as well as teaching IFS-related workshops throughout the world. To learn more, please go to www.FrankAndersonMD.com.

Dedication

To Austin, Logan, and Michael:
Where life begins and love never ends

Table of Contents

Foreword

By Richard Schwartz

Founder of Internal Family Systems Therapy

When I began the journey of exploring clients' parts that led to the development of IFS, I was a structural family therapist. The late Salvador Minuchin, the father of structural family therapy, was part of a vanguard of therapists who reacted to what they considered the obsessive tendency of psychoanalysts to focus on and ruminate about the products of their clients' minds and their histories. The structural family motto was that the past was irrelevant because you could eliminate symptoms and change emotions by simply reorganizing family relationships in the present.

Therefore, as I discovered that my clients had these inner families of parts, I focused on reorganizing the ways their parts related to one another in the present and ignored whatever came up about their pasts. For example, once a client accessed an exiled, terrified young part, I got them to hold and comfort that inner child until it felt safe and calmed down. I then had them let its protectors know they could relax. Clients would leave these sessions feeling much better, but that improvement wouldn't last. In exploring why, I learned from clients that their parts were frozen in past traumas and couldn't fully heal until that was addressed. This was very disappointing to the parts of me that wanted so much to believe that I didn't have to deal with my own traumas and only needed to occasionally hug my own inner children.

However, my protective parts were also scientific and committed to following the data, so they allowed me to begin exploring the impact of trauma on people. I became obsessed with this topic and read everything I could find on it, particularly the work of Judith Herman. This research and experimentation culminated in my coauthoring the book *Mosaic Mind* in 1996, which went into great detail about the treatment of one of my complex trauma clients.

This research also led me to the work of Bessel van der Kolk, who, more than anyone, has raised the consciousness of both psychotherapy and our culture regarding the devastating impact of trauma and how much it is the driver of psychiatric symptoms. In doing so, Bessel revolutionized the understanding of psychiatric syndromes and how to treat them. His and Judith Herman's work fortified my commitment to finding ways to release clients' parts from the traumatic scenes in which they were frozen in the past. At some point, I reached out to Bessel, and he became interested in IFS.

In 2012, my fiancée, Jeanne Catanzaro, wanted us to move to Boston, where she had gone to college. I agreed, in large part, because I hoped to collaborate more with Bessel and the thriving community of trauma experts that had grown around him. Shortly before that move, Bessel asked me to present at his annual Trauma Conference in Boston, where he introduced me to his handsome, vivacious protégé, Frank Anderson. Frank seemed very enthused about IFS, so when he called and wanted to meet with me some months later, I eagerly said yes.

I remember that meeting clearly. Frank talked about how much IFS had put the pieces together for him and how much luck he was having using it with clients. Then he suddenly said, "I plan to devote my professional life to helping you bring IFS to the world." Needless to say, I was thrilled to have such a charismatic, personable neuropsychiatrist and trauma expert join my team, although I had a skeptical part that reminded me that I'd heard similar things before from others that didn't pan out.

Despite that part's concerns, it has panned out. Frank has become a key figure in the IFS movement. Through his writing and presenting, and our brainstorming, he has contributed to fleshing out aspects of IFS related not only to trauma but also to neurobiology, medication, and parenting. His competence as a theorist and presenter has brought credibility and many new students to the IFS community. The manual he took the lead on coauthoring with Martha Sweezy and myself, *Internal Family Systems Skills Training Manual*, gives therapists a user-friendly workbook for using IFS with challenging clients and provides the scaffolding for this book.

In addition, Frank has developed a training program on IFS and trauma, as well as workshops on IFS in relation to parenting and medication, which he has taught all over the world. He recently joined the IFS Institute to develop online courses and has turned out to be a wonderful interviewer for those courses. Until recently, he also donated enormous amounts of time to running the Foundation for Self Leadership, the nonprofit organization that funds research on IFS and also supports outreach and provides scholarships. He did all this while maintaining his private practice and staying connected to his husband and sons.

So it is with huge gratitude and excitement that I write the foreword for this new offering from Frank. In it, he has the space to elaborate on how to safely and successfully use IFS with clients who have suffered from complex or developmental trauma. These tend to be the clients who trigger therapists the most. Due to the repeated and chronic abuse they suffered as children—at the hands of the people they both depended on and were trapped with—their firefighters became frighteningly extreme, and their managers became super rigid and controlling. These clients have parts that don't trust anyone and that constantly test the therapist's trustworthiness. They may find ways to punish, reject, or manipulate the therapist even when the therapist has been able to stay in Self-energy.

The field of psychiatry further triggers therapists by giving these challenging clients the scariest and most pathologized diagnoses, like borderline personality disorder, dissociative identity disorder, and manic depression. Thus, it is very easy for a therapist's protector to jump in and obscure the therapist's Self. These clients are extremely sensitive to those abandonments and will escalate their symptoms in response. As a result, working with this population can easily lead to a vicious cycle in which the therapist's and client's protectors escalate to the point where the client is retraumatized and re-betrayed.

Therapists and clients need a non-pathologizing map to navigate this potential minefield in a way that leads to healing and empowerment. IFS provides that map, but until this book, therapists have had to piece together the IFS approach to complex PTSD from the wide variety of sources out there, which describe IFS and trauma in a general way. This book offers the first comprehensive map to working with complex PTSD from an IFS perspective and, therefore, is invaluable. Not only has Frank worked extensively with these clients, but because he's a highly trained neuropsychiatrist, this book also thoroughly covers topics such as the neuroscience of trauma and the use of medication.

In addition, since Frank has worked so much with his own parts that become triggered by traumatized clients, he speaks eloquently and with refreshing self-disclosure about the importance of the therapist's steady, compassionate presence and the need to find and heal the parts that interfere with the ability to stay present even in the face of provocation. I admire Frank's vulnerability as he lets us in on his personal journey of healing and learning, which brings the book to life.

Frank has brought so much to the exploding IFS movement, and this book is a crucial contribution that brings clarity and light to the often dark, confusing journey that is the treatment of complex PTSD.

Acknowledgments

I would first like to acknowledge Linda Jackson at PESI Publishing, who believed in my ability to write this book before I embraced that belief myself. To Erik J. Martin for his extraordinary editing support. You are truly a gifted and talented writer who instantly identified my voice and helped it flow smoothly and naturally onto the page. I'm grateful to have found you. To Jenessa Jackson, who helped dot the i's and cross the t's to make this book come together in clear and wonderful ways, and to Amy Rubenzer for her creative genius on the book's cover and interior layout.

To Bessel van der Kolk and the folks at the Trauma Center, who first took me in and taught me how to sit with the unspeakable. To my clients, who educated me, taught me about the resilience of the human spirit, and helped me grow professionally as well as personally. To Dick Schwartz, my mentor, my friend, and the "channel" for and founder of Internal Family Systems (IFS). I know in my heart that our paths were meant to cross, and I feel honored and privileged to be invited to join you in this wonderful journey of bringing IFS to the world. You are a devoted healer and a true inspiration.

To my parents, who continue to show up, to see me for who I am, to accept our differences, and to love me through it all. I'm eternally grateful to you both. To Austin—my gift—your innocence, humor, and way of challenging everything has helped me grow beyond my wildest dreams. To Logan, we are on parallel but independent paths. Thank you for being the vehicle that ignited my path toward healing my trauma. And last, to Michael, my unexpected life partner. Your quiet, calm, steady, and wise presence and your unconditional love and support is truly remarkable. Our connection is the definition of relational healing. I love you from the bottom of my heart.

Introduction

I believe in a fundamental and universal truth: *Trauma blocks love and connection,* and healing our wounds provides access to the love and goodness that is inherent in us all. I further believe we each possess internal wisdom—an inner compass, a truth in feeling—and when we're connected to these inner resources, we are in alignment and can live our best authentic life. Trauma violates this connection within us and disrupts our ability to bond freely with others. For the sake of survival, we disengage from ourselves, lose connection to that which is true, avoid vulnerability, and shun communion with those around us. Our job as Internal Family Systems (IFS) therapists is to help our clients confront, come to terms with, and release the pain and anguish they carry from past experiences. The healing process enables our clients to reconnect naturally and organically to their inner virtues, allowing them to reclaim self-connection, experience self-love, transcend their trauma, and exercise the ability to unite with and love others.

THE PURPOSE OF THIS BOOK

As someone with a trauma history, it's not surprising that I've spent most of my career helping clients who struggle with multiple forms of abuse. I was extremely fortunate to be able to collaborate with and espouse the teachings of Bessel van der Kolk over the last 29 years. This true visionary has consistently pushed traditional treatment boundaries to support, promote, and study new and innovative treatments for sufferers of the unspeakable.

I met Dick Schwartz, the founder of the IFS model, at one of Bessel's annual trauma conferences, and we instantly bonded. There was an energy running through my body that felt extraordinary to me and larger than the both of us. Dick said: "Can you feel that Frank?" I did, and I instinctively knew in that moment that I was there to be of assistance to him on his journey. I'm in awe of Dick's tireless ambition to share the truths about IFS around the world and am forever grateful to him for including me on this adventure. This experience has been personally life changing, positioning me to better understand myself and to more effectively support my clients. I am a firm believer in IFS—convinced that it offers the most comprehensive approach for healing complex and dissociative trauma. IFS is also a paradigm for living: Those exposed to it live more consciously and choose to be more self-connected and openly compassionate.

My hope in writing this book is to help clinicians overcome the common pitfalls and roadblocks frequently associated with treating complex post-traumatic stress disorder (PTSD) or relational trauma by using the IFS model of therapy. Equipped with this knowledge and approach, you can help your clients learn how to effectively embrace, validate, and support the positive intentions of all the extreme symptoms that accompany their trauma. You can also learn to identify and gently be with the parts of you that get activated when working with your clients so you can more efficiently access and mend the wounds that plague them.

This book will explore the different types of trauma, examine the ways IFS is different from traditional phase-oriented treatment, demonstrate how to incorporate IFS with other models of treatment, and address protective parts in a trauma-specific manner so your clients can unlock access to the wounds they protect. Together, we will incorporate neuroscience knowledge as it relates to the IFS model and review the neurobiology of PTSD and dissociation. Additionally, we will investigate how neuroscience can inform therapeutic decisions with extreme symptoms and will discover the unique ways in which IFS addresses attachment trauma. We will delve into neglect, vulnerability, shame, and common adaptations associated with relational trauma as it relates to various parts, such as those that are critical, numbing, avoidant, passive, perpetrating, substance using, and caretaking.

What's more, we will review a range of wounds and the different types of unburdening practices associated with complex and extreme trauma. We will also cover common roadblocks to healing and discuss ways to successfully overcome them so your clients can effectively release the pain they carry. This book will incorporate case examples, personal experiences, and clinical exercises to enhance your learning as well.

Whenever I present neuroscience knowledge that I feel is relevant to the IFS model, be aware that this is only my perspective, and as IFS research evolves, we will have a more definitive explanation of how IFS therapy affects the brain and the nervous system. In recent years, our field has expanded and greatly benefitted from discoveries about the connection between neuroscience and psychotherapy. Psychotherapy has gained a new level of legitimacy within the scientific and medical community, as we are no longer seen as a "soft science." As scientific knowledge continues to explain what is occurring neurologically throughout the psychotherapeutic process, we can better use this knowledge to inform our therapeutic decision-making and continue to advance our capacity for healing overwhelming life experiences.

Ultimately, my wish as a psychiatrist, therapist, and trauma survivor is that this book will offer you a unique perspective on how to transcend relational trauma by using IFS. Welcome, and thanks for joining me on this exciting journey, which I hope will be informative, valuable, and rewarding.

SECTION I

Trauma and IFS

CHAPTER 1

Complex PTSD and IFS

RELATIONAL TRAUMA

I want to even the playing field right out of the gate. I'm not a big fan of the "us versus them" mentality that says, "I'm the doctor and you're the patient," "I'm a healer and you're a victim," or "I'm the trauma expert and you have a trauma history." I believe that we all have been traumatized in some form at some point in our lives, that we each carry wounds deep within ourselves, and that everyone works hard to keep the pain from those experiences at bay. What's more, we're each susceptible to being triggered and to overreacting when our wounds resurface, and we all have what IFS refers to as the "Self"—our core, our essence, our internal compass that possesses inherent wisdom and healing capacity.

Complex PTSD, in its most basic form, is a relational violation that disrupts our sense of trust and safety in the world and limits access to our Self-energy. Healing relational trauma puts us back in touch with our natural core and permits us to love and connect again with others. We've all felt the difference between being alone and being lonely, or spending time by yourself contentedly versus feeling isolated and yearning for some form of connection. Those who are more introverted, for example, enjoy spending time alone. It rejuvenates them in a way that allows for a peaceful and quiet internal connection. This is different from the pain, isolation, and detachment that accompanies relational trauma and wounding (e.g., feeling the hurt and betrayal of rejection, a verbal critical attack, or sexual violation).

WHAT'S COMPLEX ABOUT COMPLEX PTSD?

There are several things that make working with someone who has complex PTSD so challenging. One of them is the approach to therapy itself. When someone suffers from repeated relational trauma, they struggle with closeness, trust, and safety in relationships. That same person seeks therapy with the unspoken intention of forming a close, intimate relationship with you: their therapist. We carry the hope that they will feel safe enough to share their deepest thoughts, feelings, and fears with us so we can help them resolve their experience of relational betrayal.

However, this is a premise that virtually guarantees failure. Why? Because it is unrealistic to expect that people who have been violated by relationships will expose their vulnerabilities to a total stranger without repercussions. Under these circumstances, traumatic reenactments are practically unavoidable.

Working with relational trauma inevitably triggers a client's wounds and activates our own relational history and personal wounding. It also rekindles our personal struggles with closeness and intimacy. Remember: You likely have caretaking parts that are rooted in protecting one of your relational wounds. You probably wouldn't have chosen this profession if you weren't on some level working through your own personal relational histories, right? Yet it feels safer to help someone else with their problems than to focus on our own, and we can feel good about ourselves to boot because we're helping others. But this isn't exactly a win-win. Even though being a therapist is a noble and satisfying profession, with relational trauma, each party's painful past is likely to get reactivated and complicate the intention of helping our client heal. It's certainly possible to achieve, but it's typically much more challenging than you'd expect.

This is one of the primary reasons I wanted to write this book: to help people better navigate this complicated journey of resolving relational trauma. Gratefully, I can relate the value of my experience—as a result of my own therapy and of working closely with my clients, I have been able to heal much of my own personal trauma.

Working with trauma can be difficult, especially when it activates our own histories. It's also problematic when severe symptoms or extreme reactions surface in the treatment. For example, many clients will feel suicidal at some point in their treatment. Some will resort to self-cutting in order to soothe themselves; substance abuse is also common, as are panic attacks, depression, dissociation, and shame. *Extreme experiences warrant extreme responses.*

Attachment trauma that developed in childhood often gets reactivated in therapy, triggering a desperate need for connection, a fear of closeness, and panic related to abandonment and loss. Boundary issues inevitably get stirred up with relational trauma as well. In my experience, a therapist can tend to fall into one of two places regarding boundary issues: too much or too little. When your parts are triggered around boundaries, you can overcompensate by *offering too much,* trying to rescue them by recommending things that are outside the therapeutic norm. Alternatively, you can become *rigid and controlling* in an attempt to protect yourself from the overwhelming neediness of your client's parts.

Trauma is rarely simple and straightforward as it relates to symptom production. Many survivors of trauma also struggle with depression, anxiety, panic, substance abuse, bipolar disorder, eating issues, obsessive-compulsive disorder (OCD), and even psychosis in addition to their PTSD. Multiple comorbidities are common with clients who have been traumatized, and these biological abnormalities need to be managed to help our clients effectively address and fully heal the emotional effects of their abuse. All of these factors speak to the complicated nature of treating complex PTSD. And we as therapists need to constantly monitor our reactions, which are commonly activated throughout this process.

The following list summarizes some of the complications involved in treating complex PTSD.

> •The pitfalls of the therapy relationship
>
> •The activation of therapist parts
>
> •The presence of extreme symptoms and reactions in clients
>
> •The reenactment of early attachment trauma
>
> •The struggle with boundary-related issues
>
> •The frequency of comorbid conditions

SITTING WITH THE HORRIFIC

No matter what therapy model you practice, it's challenging to work with someone who has just described their past sexual, physical, verbal, emotional, or neglect trauma in horrific detail. Recollections like "At that moment, I thought I was going to die," "I was suffocating and gasping for air as he was on top of me," "The image of her lying facedown on the floor in a pool of blood will be embedded forever in my mind," and "As I heard each gunshot, I kept thinking to myself that the next one is for me" are jarring and disturbing to hear aloud. Listening to and processing these horrendous client memories is difficult, no matter how experienced you are in treating trauma. I will never forget what Bessel van der Kolk said during one of our team meetings at his Trauma Center many years ago: "Trauma survivors don't fear the worst-case scenario. They know it because they've lived the unthinkable." How right he is.

Let's face the facts: This is hard but rewarding work. I believe we're all drawn to this field for primarily personal reasons—myself included—and that sitting with someone as they describe and relive the unthinkable in our presence is tough to do and often activates our trauma. Yet, while I'm not perfect at this, over my career I've found that the more I heal my own trauma, the easier it is for me to work with my clients and help them process their horrific experiences. I'm better positioned to stay present, maintain a compassionate stance, and avoid getting so empathically overwhelmed like I used to. IFS has helped me clear out so much of my traumatic history and exorcise my demons that I'm better able to treat clients without getting triggered myself or trying to rescue them as I did in the past. Make no mistake: It has taken me several years and a lot of personal therapy to arrive at this safer, calmer, and clearer place. But today, after unburdening many of my wounds and reconciling my negative experiences, I'm better able to serve my clients.

THE UNIQUE CONTRIBUTION OF IFS

The IFS model of therapy is rooted in systems thinking and the multiplicity of the mind. It believes that all individuals have what is called a *Self* (our core, soul, or internal leader), which doesn't need to be cultivated or developed; we are born with it. It also acknowledges that we have *parts* or aspects of our personality that we are born with too, which have positive intentions and are not a sign of pathology. With trauma, parts are forced to take on extreme protective roles or to carry painful experiences.

IFS has a unique way of addressing and dealing with trauma, and for me it's the most complete model I've come across to date. It deals with the *cognitive* by addressing and unloading distorted thoughts and beliefs, it incorporates the *body* as it supports the movement and discharge of physical sensations, and it facilitates the release of painful *feelings* (such as unworthiness, loneliness, and unlovability) by healing the wounds that parts of us carry. IFS helps release parts from their extreme roles and repairs the chasm created between parts and the Self as a result of the trauma. Parts are then able to restore trust in Self-leadership and fluidly integrate back into the whole system. IFS incorporates spirituality and promotes a humane, non-pathologizing, openhearted, and loving approach to healing the pain associated with repeated relational violations. I can personally attest to its power and efficacy. Being part of the solution, with love and compassion, perfectly aligns with who I am and who I want to be in and for the world.

GLOSSARY OF IFS TERMS*

5 P's: The qualities of a skilled IFS therapist: presence, patience, persistence, perspective, and playfulness.

6 F's: The steps used when working with protective parts: find the part, focus on it, flesh it out, feel toward it, befriend it, and find out its fear.

8 C's: The qualities of Self-energy: compassion, curiosity, calm, clarity, connectedness, confidence, courage, and creativity.

Blended: When a part takes over, making it indistinguishable from another part or from the Self.

Burdened: When a part holds negative beliefs (e.g., "I'm unlovable," "I'm worthless"), intense trauma-related feelings (e.g., terror, panic, shame, rage), or physical sensations (e.g., body memories, visual flashbacks).

Direct access: A method of communication with parts. When a part is blended and the client's Self is not accessible, the therapist speaks directly to the client's part. This is an alternative form of communication when internal communication or *insight* is blocked.

Do-over: One of the steps of the unburdening process. After the Self has witnessed what an exiled part wants to share, the Self joins the part, going back to a time in the part's past, and offers the part a fully corrective experience.

Exile (wounded part): A part that carries painful thoughts, feelings, and physical sensations as a result of traumatic or overwhelming experiences. The client expends a great deal of energy to keep exiled parts out of conscious awareness. Examples include parts that feel alone, unloved, shamed, or worthless.

Firefighter (reactive/extreme part): A protective part that typically emerges after a wounded part is triggered. Firefighters respond in an extreme and sometimes overreactive fashion, typically don't care about the well-being of others and will do whatever is necessary to end an exiled part's pain. Examples of firefighter responses include suicide, cutting, drinking, binging, raging, shaming, and dissociating.

Integration: One of the steps of the unburdening process. After the exiled part is healed, we bring protective parts back and suggest the release of their protective role.

---

* Some of these definitions were taken from the *Internal Family Systems Skills Training Manual* (Anderson et al., 2017).

Internal communication (insight): The primary approach therapists use to help clients communicate with their parts. The client's Self is able to listen to and communicate with a part. When parts block internal communication, we use direct access.

Invitation to exiled parts: One of the steps of the unburdening process. After the exiled part unloads the burden, it can internalize new qualities with which it chooses to fill the space the wound left behind.

Invitation to protective parts: An offer to a protective part when requesting permission to access a wounded part. During the invitation, the therapist can help guarantee that another part will not overwhelm the system, will propose a new role for the protective part, and will offer to heal the wound.

Manager (preventive part): One of two protective parts. The manager's goal is to keep exiled parts hidden by making sure the wound never gets activated. Manager types include conflict-avoidant, intellectual, obsessing, worrying, and hardworking parts.

Overwhelm: A primary fear in trauma and one of the offers to a protective part in the invitation. During the invitation, the therapist will directly ask an intense part not to overwhelm the system, which can make a protective part more willing to allow access to a wound that needs to be healed.

Parts: Separate mental states or subpersonalities within each person that IFS therapists classify into three broad categories: exiles (wounded parts), managers (preventive parts), and firefighters (reactive/extreme parts). Parts are separate from the Self.

Polarization: A conflict that typically, but not exclusively, occurs between two protective parts that often safeguard the same wound in an opposing manner. Polarizations can become extreme and costly, especially with trauma, and resolution occurs when the Self validates each side and parts allow the Self to resolve the dilemma.

Retrieval: One of the steps of the unburdening process. Once an exiled part is identified and given a corrective experience by the Self, it's free to leave the past and exist somewhere safe in the present day.

Self: An innate presence in each of us that promotes balance, harmony, and nonjudgmental qualities (such as curiosity, caring, creativity, courage, calm, connectedness, clarity, and compassion). The Self is a state of being that can neither be created nor destroyed.

Self-energy: The quality and essence of a client's Self that the therapist directs toward the client's internal parts and external relationships.

Unblending (separating): A mental state of differentiation where parts can be present for, yet remain separate from and not dominate or overwhelm, the Self.

Unburdening: The process of healing wounded parts or exiles. The steps include witnessing, do-over, retrieval, unload, invitation, and integration.

Unloading: One of the steps of the unburdening process. Once the wounded part is safely in the present, it is allowed to release the thoughts, feelings, and physical sensations it carried with regard to the trauma.

Updating: The process of introducing a part (protective or exiled) who is in connection with the Self of the past to the current-day Self.

Witnessing: One of the steps of the unburdening process. The exiled part can show and/or tell the Self about its experience in a way that allows the part to feel fully seen, understood, heard, and validated.

CHAPTER 2

Various Types of Trauma

Not all traumas are the same, nor should they be treated equally. The following section provides a brief description of the various types or categories of trauma. Typically, individuals can experience a single traumatic event or what is referred to as acute stress disorder and, for the most part, have a high likelihood of fully recovering from the experience within one month. However, if they have several traumatic events in their lives, they are more likely to experience chronic trauma and have symptoms of PTSD that persist beyond one month. When these traumatic experiences involve repeated relational violations in childhood, individuals can acquire developmental trauma disorder (DTD) or attachment trauma, and when these symptoms or violations persist or occur in adulthood, it can result in a diagnosis of complex PTSD or relational trauma. Under more extreme circumstances and following early, repeated, and/or severe abuse, a diagnosis of dissociative identity disorder (DID) is common, which consists of multiple discrete parts that operate independently of each other.

SINGLE-INCIDENT TRAUMA OR ACUTE STRESS DISORDER

Single-incident or acute trauma typically results from a lone traumatic event that occurs in someone's life, such as a car accident, sudden death of a loved one, physical assault, robbery, or acute medical illness. The resulting symptoms (e.g., intrusive images, negative mood, dissociation, avoidance, numbing, and arousal) are similar to those experienced by chronic PTSD. With acute stress disorder, however, the symptoms are normal physiological adaptations to an acute event that typically resolve within one month of the trauma occurring (SAMHSA, 2014). A survey conducted in 24 countries across the world found that over 70 percent of people report experiencing at least one traumatic event in their lifetime, and 30.5 percent report being exposed to four or more traumas (Benjet et al., 2016).

We should respond differently to acute trauma than to chronic trauma or complex PTSD. With acute trauma, it's more important to provide a safe holding environment so clients are naturally and organically able to process the event. PTSD symptoms are normal within the first month of a trauma and, to date, we don't have a specific protocol in IFS to treat acute trauma. However, I've seen IFS be extremely effective, especially when clients can access Self-energy. The Self provides the corrective nurturing environment for parts and helps them avoid taking on any extreme role of protection or the need to carry the pain in isolation. *In acute trauma, the Self's presence can prevent the development of protective parts and exiled wounds.*

Eye movement desensitization and reprocessing (EMDR) is an established and well-known treatment for acute stress disorder and has sufficient research to support its use with acute trauma (Buydens, Wilensky, & Hensley, 2014). Critical incident stress debriefing (CISD) has historically been a common treatment for acute trauma, especially when it occurs in groups, but its efficacy has come into question, and the protocol is currently being reevaluated to determine the correct amount of processing that is beneficial after a traumatic event (Wessely & Deahl, 2003). Talking too much or not enough can both be problematic. Certain medications, such as benzodiazepines, should also be avoided during the acute phase of a trauma because they can interfere with normal memory processing and can increase the likelihood of developing chronic PTSD (Guina et al., 2015). There is, however, emerging research showing that steroid use can be helpful during the acute phase of trauma and might help prevent the development of chronic PTSD (Rasmusson et al., 2017).

PTSD OR CHRONIC TRAUMA

There are several known risk factors that determine whether or not someone will remain symptomatic and develop chronic PTSD after an acute traumatic event. Some include individuals who have experienced a prior trauma, those who have mental health–related issues, those who struggle with substance abuse, and those who have a genetic history of PTSD. Here is an overview of the diagnostic criteria for PTSD from SAMSHA's Treatment Improvement Protocol (TIP) Series (SAMSHA, 2014):

a. Exposure to actual or threatened death, serious injury, or sexual violence

b. Presence of intrusive symptoms associated with the traumatic event

c. Persistent avoidance of stimuli associated with the traumatic event

d. Negative alterations in cognition and mood associated with the event

e. Marked alterations in arousal and reactivity associated with the event

f. The duration of the disturbance is more than one month

g. Symptoms cause clinically significant distress or impairment in social, occupational, or other important areas of functioning

h. Symptoms are not attributed to the physiological effects of a substance or other medical condition

As we know, PTSD can result from a variety of different kinds of trauma, such as a car accident, the loss of a loved one, a date rape, witnessing someone else's trauma, or living through a global pandemic. It can result from a single acute event that turns chronic, or it can occur after several related events.

COMPLEX PTSD OR RELATIONAL TRAUMA

When trauma is repetitive and relational in nature, it's called complex PTSD or relational trauma. According to Judy Herman, the author of the classic book *Trauma and Recovery*, complex PTSD is the result of exposure to repeated or prolonged instances or multiple forms of interpersonal trauma, often occurring under circumstances where escape is not possible due to physical, psychological, maturational, family, environmental, or social constraints (Herman, 1992).

The International Society for Traumatic Stress Studies (ISTSS) developed a task force to define and develop treatment guidelines for complex PTSD. Their definition includes the core symptoms of PTSD in conjunction with disturbances in five domains of self-regulatory capacities, including: (1) emotion regulation difficulties, (2) disturbances in relational capacities, (3) alterations in attention and consciousness (e.g., dissociation), (4) adversely affected belief systems, and (5) somatic distress or disorganization (Cloitre et al., 2012). Bessel van der Kolk and others have alternately named the syndrome "disorder of extreme stress not otherwise specified (DESNOS)" (Pelcovitz et al., 1997).

This is the type of trauma that we will be primarily focusing on in this book. It is the most common form of trauma to show up in your office, and it's difficult to treat and likely to activate your parts. But when it's healed, it can have a dramatic effect on the quality of your clients' lives. I believe IFS is perfectly suited to this task because of its ability to provide relief and healing of wounded parts that carry the effects of repeated relational violations.

DEVELOPMENTAL TRAUMA

There are two different ways to view developmental trauma. One is more common and widely recognized. This is relational trauma or complex trauma in childhood, also known as developmental trauma disorder (van der Kolk, 2005). This perspective of developmental trauma is supported by the Adverse Childhood Experiences (ACE) study performed by Kaiser Permanente and the Centers for Disease Control and Prevention, which showed that 11 percent of respondents reported emotional abuse in childhood, 30 percent reported physical abuse, and 20 percent reported sexual abuse (Felitti et al., 1998). In addition, 24 percent reported exposure to family alcohol abuse, 19 percent were exposed to mental illness, 13 percent witnessed their mother being battered, and 5 percent reported family drug abuse. These numbers are alarmingly high and much more common than we previously acknowledged.

Felitti and colleagues also found a high correlation between a person's ACE score and negative health outcomes later in life, such as depression, suicide attempts, alcoholism, drug abuse, sexual promiscuity, domestic violence, cigarette smoking, obesity, physical inactivity, and sexually transmitted diseases. Additionally, individuals with higher ACE scores had a higher risk of heart disease, cancer, diabetes, skeletal fractures, and liver disease. This alarming report is consistent with the view of Gabor Maté, author of *When the Body Says No: Exploring the Stress-Disease Connection*, who maintains that most medical and mental health problems are rooted in trauma.

Another way to approach developmental trauma is to ask the question: *At what developmental stage did the trauma occur?* This perspective looks at the impact a traumatic experience has on brain development, symptom production, and psychiatric diagnosis. Martin Teicher, the director of the Developmental Biopsychiatry Research Program at Harvard Medical School, and his lab have shown that childhood maltreatment alters brain structure and function, depending on the type of abuse and stage of development. His group identified "sensitive periods" when certain brain regions are maximally vulnerable to different types of trauma. For example, they have demonstrated how verbal abuse is associated with alterations in the auditory cortex and language production and how witnessing domestic violence is connected with changes in the visual cortex and the limbic system. Their research shows us how various traumas, at different ages, affect different parts of the brain and create different symptoms and different psychiatric disorders (Teicher & Samson, 2016)

Another pioneer in the study of developmental trauma is Bruce Perry, the creator of the Neurosequential Model of Therapeutics. He looks at the ways trauma and neglect change the biology of the brain and affect childhood cognitive, behavioral, emotional, social, and physiological development. As we continue to identify which brain regions are affected by different types of trauma at various developmental stages, we can begin to develop brain-specific interventions to help treat and potentially reverse the physiologic abnormalities created by each specific trauma. It's important to remember that we never stop developing. A traumatic loss will affect us differently at age 12 versus age 30 or 60 because of its differing effect on our brain, body, and emotional capacity at each developmental stage.

EXTREME OR DISSOCIATIVE TRAUMA

The last type of trauma is extreme or dissociative. I personally see dissociation as a *spectrum disorder*, meaning that there is often a range of dissociative parts, from the most benign (e.g., a part spacing out) to the most extreme (e.g., many different parts appearing separate from one another with no overlapping memory or time awareness, as is the case in DID). With trauma, dissociative parts are often extreme in nature, as they respond to what they believe is a life-or-death situation and then correspondingly disengage, detach, or numb out as a survival mechanism. (More on this later as we explore the neurobiology of PTSD and dissociation.)

Many therapists get easily overwhelmed by clients who struggle with DID because they are masters of deception who are often extremely confusing at first and overly dramatic in presentation, and they frequently present with what appears to be one unsolvable dilemma after another. It's important to stay steady with the IFS principles and not get too caught up in the drama; some parts protect, some parts carry wounds, and, somewhere deep inside, Self-energy helps heal the pain.

The following chart provides a summary of the different categories of trauma.

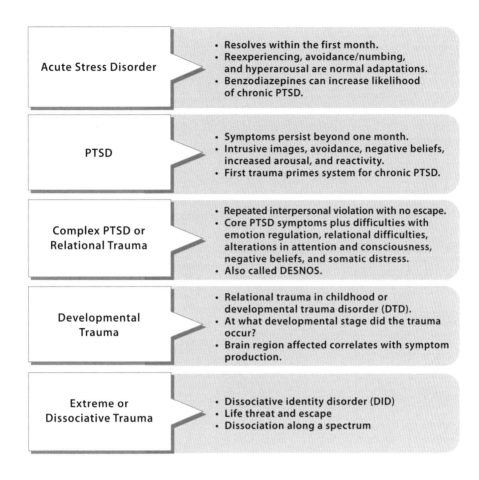

Acute Stress Disorder

- Resolves within the first month.
- Reexperiencing, avoidance/numbing, and hyperarousal are normal adaptations.
- Benzodiazepines can increase likelihood of chronic PTSD.

PTSD

- Symptoms persist beyond one month.
- Intrusive images, avoidance, negative beliefs, increased arousal, and reactivity.
- First trauma primes system for chronic PTSD.

Complex PTSD or Relational Trauma

- Repeated interpersonal violation with no escape.
- Core PTSD symptoms plus difficulties with emotion regulation, relational difficulties, alterations in attention and consciousness, negative beliefs, and somatic distress.
- Also called DESNOS.

Developmental Trauma

- Relational trauma in childhood or developmental trauma disorder (DTD).
- At what developmental stage did the trauma occur?
- Brain region affected correlates with symptom production.

Extreme or Dissociative Trauma

- Dissociative identity disorder (DID)
- Life threat and escape
- Dissociation along a spectrum

CHAPTER 3

IFS: Permanent Healing of Emotional Wounds

THE MODEL

I believe that the IFS model is unique in some of the ways it supports healing, especially as it relates to trauma. I also find it the most comprehensive and the best fit for my personality and style of psychotherapy. Here is a brief overview of the IFS model, in case you are new to IFS. For a complete overview, including step-by-step explanations, exercises, and clinical examples, please refer to the *IFS Skills Training Manual* (Anderson et al., 2017).

I have a great deal of admiration for IFS founder Dick Schwartz and the way he allowed (and continues to allow) the model to unfold organically. He is steadfast in staying true to what his clients have told him about their internal experiences. Dick enabled IFS to evolve in a grassroots fashion, serving as a model of the people.

THREE MAIN PARTS

In IFS, there are three types of parts we commonly encounter: (1) exiles or *parts that carry wounds*, (2) managers or *preventive parts*, and (3) firefighters or *extreme, reactive parts* (Schwartz & Sweezy, 2020). Each of these parts is a normal aspect or component of our client's personality until it needs to take on a specific role within the system (i.e., to protect or to carry a wound as a result of some overwhelming or traumatic life experience). In this book, we will refer to the manager protective parts as *preventive* and the firefighter protective parts as *reactive* or *extreme*, and we will refer to the exiled parts as *wounded* or *those who carry the pain*.

I often refer to *preventive parts* as the unsung heroes. They run our day-to-day life, they're hard-working and often exhausted, and they don't get the credit they deserve. They rarely get a break, and these are the parts that love taking medications in search of some relief. Some common examples are pleasing parts, parts that want to be liked, and parts that are funny, obsessive, or conflict-avoidant or that want to look good. They tend to have a hard time separating or unblending because they run the show and often will say things like: "What do you mean by 'separate'? I am Lily." They like to feel and appear as if they're in charge and under control.

Extreme or reactive parts are plentiful in clients who have suffered from trauma and tend to be the most challenging and troublesome for therapists. Remember: Extreme circumstances require extreme responses. In treating relational trauma, which tends to be long-term, repetitive, and ongoing, these parts are often tenacious, absolute, and highly triggering to those who encounter them. Most of the psychotherapy consultations I provide for therapists are about their own parts that get activated by extreme parts of clients.

Society, culture, partners, and family members tend to hate these extreme, reactive parts (and these parts know it too). But continuing education organizations and conference organizers tend to love them because therapists are constantly looking for new ways to work with these challenging parts. Some examples are cutting parts, suicidal parts, parts that numb out and dissociate, parts that abuse substances, parts that overeat or under eat, parts that shame, and parts that are critical or perpetrate. The list can go on and on.

These diverse and numerous parts are actually among my principal motivations for writing this book. I have a deep desire to assist therapists in guiding their clients to overcome relational trauma, but in order to help someone heal, we need to be calm, efficient, composed, and confident when encountering these extreme parts in order to get their permission to access the wound.

The *wounded parts* are the young, sensitive, and vulnerable aspects of our personalities. They were forced to carry the hurt, pain, sense of betrayal, sadness, loneliness, shame, neglect, and lack of love as it related to the painful and difficult moments in our lives. We can, of course, get hurt and sustain wounds at any stage of our lives. Relational trauma can occur in childhood from abusive caregivers or bullies at school, as well as in adulthood from abusive partners or unhealthy colleagues at work.

Painful experiences can be held and expressed in many different forms. Parts can communicate through body sensations, emotions, thoughts, or beliefs. They can reveal what they are holding through visual, auditory, or other sensory modalities. It's important for therapists to help clients align with the part's preferred method of communication. For example, they can *listen* to a part that communicates through sound or *see* a part that expresses itself visually. If a client tries to *hear* what a more tactile part is expressing through *physical sensation*, communication is misaligned, and the desired result will not be achieved.

I believe that exiles live primarily in implicit memory, and flashbacks are wounded parts sharing fragments of what they're holding through one of the five senses. After all, wounds do not define parts; when we help them unload what they carry, they once again become the loving, fun, and creative aspects of our personality that were always there but were temporarily obscured by the trauma.

WE ALL HAVE A SELF

One of the great contributions of the IFS model to the field of psychotherapy is the recognition of the Self. Dick Schwartz didn't invent Self-energy, but he certainly brought awareness to it by attentively listening to his clients with an open heart and genuine interest.

We have further clarified the Self as being different from parts. As mentioned earlier, we are each born with a Self that possesses an internal wisdom and the natural intrinsic capacity to heal. It has been called the core seat of consciousness—our soul, a spiritual space that is connected to love, nature, and the divine. The IFS model describes the 8 C's of Self-energy as: (1) calm, (2) curiosity, (3) compassion, (4) connectedness, (5) creativity, (6) courage, (7) clarity, and (8) confidence (Schwartz & Sweezy, 2020). I describe the Self as *a state of being*; one truly "gets it" when they experience Self-energy or embody it personally. It can be experienced differently by different people. For me, it was initially a theoretical construct until halfway through my Level 2 training. I remember the moment when I felt the Self for the first time. It was like a tingling energy and simultaneous sense of calm moving throughout my whole body.

DIFFERENT FROM PHASE-ORIENTED TREATMENT

Most psychotherapy modalities that focus on treating trauma survivors support a phase-oriented approach. The ISTSS Expert Consensus Guidelines for Complex PTSD describe three distinct, well-recognized phases:

- Phase 1 focuses on enhancing the individual's safety, reducing symptoms, and increasing important emotional, social, and psychological competencies.
- Phase 2 focuses on processing the unresolved aspects of the individual's memories of the traumatic experiences. This phase emphasizes the review and reappraisal of traumatic memories in order to integrate them into an adaptive representation of one's self, one's relationships, and the world.
- Phase 3, the final phase of treatment, involves the consolidation of treatment gains to facilitate the transition from the end of the treatment to greater engagement in relationships, work, education, and community life (Cloitre et al., 2012).

The IFS model endorses certain steps that help achieve the desired outcome in a slightly different way. For example, we follow 6 F's when working with protective parts: (1) find, (2) focus, (3) flesh out, (4) feel toward, (5) befriend, and (6) find out the fear. We also abide by the six steps of the unburdening process: (1) witness, (2) do-over, (3) retrieve, (4) unload, (5) invitation, and (6) integration (Schwartz & Sweezy, 2020). However, IFS doesn't subscribe to a phase-oriented treatment approach for several important reasons. First, the message can be off-putting to some protective parts. For example, phase one (safety stabilization) embraces certain qualities of some parts more than others. A therapist might say: "I think it would be a good idea if you would meditate more, try eating healthier, and start exercising again." The suicidal, depressed, and binging parts of the client hear this as: "She's not interested in us or what we have to say or how we are trying our best to help. She cares more about those parts than she does about us." *Phase one can give the wrong message to hard-working extreme parts: that they're really not wanted.*

Another difference between the IFS view and the phase one suggestion of increasing competencies is that, in IFS, we believe everyone has a Self; we are born with what we need (Schwartz & Sweezy, 2020). Self-energy has innate healing capacities that unfold naturally. Many clients believe they have an internal deficit, exclaiming: "I'm broken. I'm empty. I have no Self." In these instances, I politely reply: "We can agree to disagree. I believe you have all that you need inside to heal your trauma. I am here to help you *access it*, not cultivate or grow it."

Another important difference between IFS and the phase-oriented approach is that IFS offers a way to deal directly with overwhelming feelings (see chapter 9), as opposed to building up strengths and resources the client can use to manage the intensity of the traumatic effect. Dick Schwartz taught us that if you talk directly to the part that holds the overwhelming feelings and ask it not to overwhelm the client, it will comply in order to receive help and experience relief.

Last, IFS teaches that healing is connected to helping burdened parts release or unload traumatic feelings and experiences they've been forced to carry, allowing them to return to their pre-burdened existence. This is different from the phase-oriented treatment method of processing, reviewing, and reappraising traumatic memories to integrate the experience into an adaptive representation of the self. In a conversation I had with him, Dick described IFS as a constraint-release model of healing as opposed to a review-reappraisal model of healing.

I remember my first exposure to IFS, which was during a one-day introductory workshop that Dick gave at one of Bessel van der Kolk's annual trauma conferences. I had been working in the trauma field for several years at this point and was used to the concept of parts. Our treatment goal was all about helping our clients process their traumatic experiences and having their parts work together in a harmonious way—consistent with the phase-oriented perspective. When I heard Dick talk about healing the wound and getting the part out of the past and into the present, it was a game changer for me. This was a totally new idea for our field, and I was hooked and wanted to learn more.

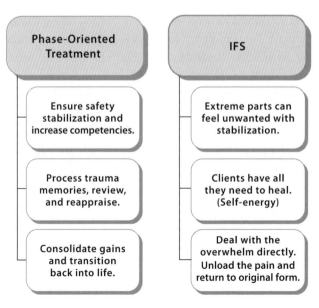

CHAPTER 4

Integrate IFS into Your Treatment Approach

DIFFERENT WAYS TO TREAT TRAUMA

Several different psychotherapy modalities can be effective for the treatment of complex PTSD, each with their unique dimensions, including IFS, EMDR, sensorimotor psychotherapy (SP), somatic experiencing (SE), and accelerated experiential dynamic processing (AEDP). Most of these models go beyond the cognitive domain and are referred to as experiential therapies, meaning that the body, emotions, and relationships are central, and clients have the resources to heal.

Many therapists who want to learn how to treat complex PTSD effectively will train in several of these modalities. Most of us end up with our own approach, which is usually an amalgam of different aspects of various models that we uniquely combine to create a way of successfully working with clients.

INTEGRATING IFS: WE ALL HAVE OUR OWN MODEL

The way I teach how to integrate IFS with other models is to proceed with an overall IFS framework as you incorporate different aspects of other models. For example, assume that everyone has parts, including parts that protect and parts that carry wounds, and that we each have inherent wisdom and healing capacity to mend our scars: the Self. However, don't proceed with any intervention without getting permission from the client's parts first. It's okay to apply different methods for treating clients and to utilize the clinical knowledge you've accumulated over the years, but it's important to incorporate them carefully in treatment. This requires letting go of your agenda and interpretations and trusting the client's Self-wisdom. *Remember: Never proceed without receiving all parts' permission first.*

For example, you may want to set up an EMDR protocol with a particularly stubborn protective part that is not willing to separate, to do somatic work with a part that looks like it is carrying a lot of physical activation in the body, or to apply cognitive behavioral therapy (CBT) with a part that is holding on to a distorted belief. You may also want to engage in AEDP, a type of relational therapy, with a young wounded part that seems desperate for connection. But always remember to ask the client to check inside and see if their parts are willing to separate, and make sure all of their parts agree before proceeding.

In my own experience, I trained first in EMDR and next in SP. After I learned about IFS, I started noticing that any EMDR protocol I established was usually with a protective part that was unwilling to separate. When identifying negative cognitions in EMDR, I was careful to first focus on protector-related beliefs (such as "I'm angry" or "I'm an alcoholic") instead of exiled beliefs (like "I'm unlovable" or "I'm worthless"). I found that doing an EMDR protocol with wounded parts without permission from protective parts resulted in unwanted abreactions or protector backlash.

The same was true regarding SP. I would embark on a piece of body work with a client and begin to notice that I was again dealing with a particular protective part. I carefully observed how the part held posture in my client's body, the way it expressed itself through physical sensations, and the movements it needed to release what it was holding. Early in my IFS career, I would often turn to EMDR and SP when I was stuck or unable to help my client move forward with IFS. Fortunately, the more proficient I became with IFS, the less I relied on the other modalities to help my clients salve their emotional scars.

What's Important for Healing?

Putting each model aside for a moment, I've spent a good deal of time thinking about the key elements or necessary components for healing trauma. Why are some clients able to accomplish this goal with relative ease while others take decades to let go of their burdens? How much of this is about their inherent capacity versus the severity of the trauma they've endured? What are the essential elements required for permanent healing to occur?

One thing I've consistently observed in most, if not all, effective trauma treatments is separation. In other words, being with, not within, one's experience appears to be a key component to healing. I often say and clinically observe that *nothing therapeutic happens in reenactment.* Neuroplasticity holds that every time a network fires, it strengthens and grows. Therefore, reliving or reenacting the dysregulated neural networks of trauma reinforces them. Mindful separation, on the other hand, can support the necessary distance, perspective, and environment for healing to occur. IFS, EMDR, SE, and SP all have a "be with" component built into their models. For example, EMDR incorporates the phrase "sit on the bus and watch the trauma go by." SP instructs clients to drop the content of the story and notice their physical sensations. IFS encourages parts to step back, relax, and allow separation from the Self.

We also know that the therapeutic relationship and quality of the connection between the therapist and the client are extremely important. Creating the necessary level of comfort allows wounded parts to safely expose their vulnerability in the service of recovering from the trauma.

The IFS Technique: Working with Protective Parts

CHAPTER 5

Getting Started and the Steps Involved

STARTING AN **IFS** SESSION

I frequently get asked questions like: "Do you do any psychoeducation about the IFS model before you start with a client?" and "How do you start a typical session?" I usually don't do any psychoeducation before I begin working with a client, and I typically initiate a session as most therapists do. I ask open-ended therapist questions, such as: "What brings you in today?" or "How can I be helpful?" I'm typically curious to get to know the general landscape of parts, I'm interested in mapping out the various systems that emerge, and I'm hoping to get a list of wounds and determine an order of healing as exiles slowly reveal themselves.

Initially, clients will launch into a series of complaints. I'll hear comments like: "I'm so glad I was able to get an appointment. I've really been struggling with my kids lately. They're at a challenging age right now, and I'm not handling things very well. My wife and I aren't on the same page at all about how to handle them, so we're fighting a lot more lately. And to top it all off, my mother just broke her hip, and I'm super stressed about taking care of her with everything else I have on my plate right now."

I may reply with: "Well, that all makes a lot of sense to me. Let me see if I have this right: One part of you isn't handling things with your kids the way you wish, one part of you is fighting more with your wife lately, and another part of you worries about taking care of your mother. Is that right?"

"Yes, exactly," I'll often hear the client say.

My recommended approach is to listen to the client's range of complaints. Then I repeat these complaints back to them, using their language and making sure they feel heard and validated. I also attach the word "part" to each of their struggles. ("One part of you is struggling with parenting duties.") My rationale here is that I'm introducing the idea that they have different parts. Clients typically don't take offense to this approach.

Next, I ask: "Which issue would you like to focus on first?" or "Which part is the most distressing to you right now?" Here I'm searching for the target part and will often suggest that the person *go inside and check*. "Going inside" is another new concept for them to consider.

This often elicits a response like: "What do you mean by 'go inside'?"

I respond with: "You know—what does your gut tell you?" or "What is your sense about where we should start?" Most people know what this means and will begin to focus their attention internally.

Using this approach, we have successfully initiated IFS therapy—with no psychoeducation about IFS or how it works.

THE 6 F'S

Once you and your client have identified a target part, this begins the sometimes complicated journey of gaining permission to access the client's wound. This tends to be easier said than done, especially with clients who have extreme histories of trauma and neglect. And this is where therapists can easily get frustrated, lose confidence, and resort back to their old ways of conducting therapy.

It's important to remember that the overarching goal of protective parts is to keep the hurt away. Protective parts will go to any length to distract, derail, confuse, and avoid moving toward the pain that an exiled part carries. Don't take it personally when a client goes against your suggestion or wishes. Try to stay the course, and remember that protective parts may feel like you're going against their purpose and agenda: to keep the pain away.

When encountering a range of protective parts, our goal is to identify which one the client's system chooses to target, knowing that all protective parts have a wound beneath them they are shielding. We then help the client get to know the part independent of itself, acclimate with the system to which it's connected, and facilitate the part separating or unblending from the Self.

Once we establish an internal relationship, it's important to foster a trusting relationship between the client's Self and this part. Harnessing the healing capacity of Self-energy, we have our clients share their love, clarity, and compassion for that part whenever it surfaces during a session. After establishing a safe relationship, we help the client learn about the part's job and the fear associated with it, knowing that the underlying fear often connects to the wound in important ways. Once the fear and wound are determined, we provide an alternative solution to their situation by offering to help heal the wound they are protecting. *Your genuine attempt to listen to and understand the positive intention of protective parts will go a long way toward convincing them to permit you to access the wounded part.* It doesn't matter which protective part you start with, as they all lead to wounds.

Listed here is an important chart that includes what we call the 6 F's and the steps involved in identifying and working with protective parts, which I just generally described. Use this chart as a template to help you remember the steps when you're working with clients. You can also refer to the *IFS Skills Training Manual* (Anderson et al., 2017) to learn greater details about the basics of the IFS model. It contains step-by-step instructions along with easy-to-use exercises and case examples.

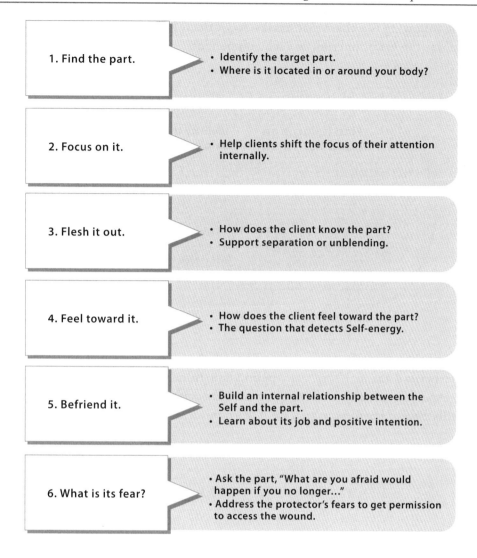

1. Find the part.
- Identify the target part.
- Where is it located in or around your body?

2. Focus on it.
- Help clients shift the focus of their attention internally.

3. Flesh it out.
- How does the client know the part?
- Support separation or unblending.

4. Feel toward it.
- How does the client feel toward the part?
- The question that detects Self-energy.

5. Befriend it.
- Build an internal relationship between the Self and the part.
- Learn about its job and positive intention.

6. What is its fear?
- Ask the part, "What are you afraid would happen if you no longer..."
- Address the protector's fears to get permission to access the wound.

EXPANDING THE 6 F's FOR TRAUMA

One of the challenges for IFS therapists is how difficult it can be to negotiate with protective parts and gain their approval to approach the exiled part. Trauma protectors are tricky, tenacious, and downright dangerous at times. It requires skills beyond the basics to effectively maneuver within the labyrinth of protective parts associated with trauma.

I generally like to break down the 6 F's into three different components. First, *identify a target part and achieve separation or unblending* (i.e., the first three steps of the 6 F's). Second, once that's successful, focus on helping the client *access Self-energy—* no easy task when it comes to complex PTSD, neglect, and DID—which we will expand on later in this book. Third, *build the internal relationship and determine the part's job and fear.* I find breaking down the 6 F's into these three different components prevents you from getting lost, derailed, or confused by the process. Remember that protective parts don't want you to go to those painful places, and they'll do just about anything to distract you.

The following is a chart that breaks down the 6 F's into these three components and explains the main function of each component.

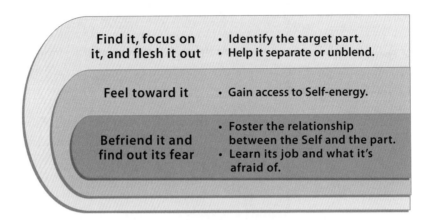

Find it, focus on it, and flesh it out	• Identify the target part. • Help it separate or unblend.
Feel toward it	• Gain access to Self-energy.
Befriend it and find out its fear	• Foster the relationship between the Self and the part. • Learn its job and what it's afraid of.

Once you get familiar and comfortable with the 6 F's, it usually requires additional expertise beyond the 6 F's to gain permission from protective parts to access the wound, especially when you're engaging parts associated with complex trauma. I call these skills *Beyond the 6 F's*, which we'll learn more about in chapter 9.

CHAPTER 6

The First Three Steps: Identify the Target Part and Help It Separate

IDENTIFYING THE TARGET: VALIDATE FIRST

As stated previously, the first three steps of the 6 F's—find, focus, and flesh out—are used to identify the target part and to help it begin to separate or unblend. This is often more difficult than expected, especially in complex PTSD. Because of the intensity of trauma, many clients spend a great deal of time *within* their parts, moving from one crisis and one protective part to another, with very little access to Self-energy.

Identifying the target part can be tricky and frustrating to achieve, especially when someone is frequently triggered and often within their experience. When clients are blended, it can be incredibly important and often challenging to validate and acknowledge what they're experiencing in the present moment, particularly if it's largely a distorted version of what's happening in reality. Remember, there's often a sliver of truth to any triggered situation. Validating the part's experience first goes a long way toward gaining permission in the end.

I personally find it challenging to validate my client's parts, especially when they are triggered and their traumatized parts have a distorted view about me. For example, I've heard clients say: "I saw the way you looked away just then. You're not interested in taking me on as a client. Most of my old therapists have called me a borderline. I'll bet you agree."

When my parts are not activated and I'm in Self-energy, I can reply as such: "It sounds like there's a part of you that's worried I won't like you or be willing to work with you. Is that correct?" But when the distortion activates my parts, I've been known to respond with: "Actually, that's not how I'm feeling. I know myself pretty well, and I'm happy to tell you what I'm feeling if you want me to."

Correcting the distortion will further inflame the client's parts, while providing validation first is usually more proficient and effective, and it allows their parts to soften and their Self to more easily emerge.

Identifying the target part involves knowing, seeing, and validating it, even if its perspective is largely from another time and place. Identifying a target part is the first step toward unblending. By recognizing, validating, and naming the target part, the client is less likely to remain blended in their experience. This opens the door for further exploration and separation, and it enables the target part to more easily connect with the Self. The key for us as therapists is to avoid getting triggered by the distortion, no matter how outrageous it may seem to you in the moment.

MIND AND BRAIN

Research from the field of neuroscience can help provide an understanding of how different parts express themselves. This provides therapists with a greater ability to sit with, identify, and validate the trauma distortions that are commonly associated with triggered parts. I love how Dan Siegel's work in particular helps us understand the difference between the mind and the brain, which has several implications when it comes to IFS. He describes the mind as an embodied and relational, self-organizing emergent process that regulates the flow of energy and information both within and between (Siegel, 2017). He also says the mind deals with energy and the prefrontal cortex (PFC), the anterior portion of the brain that integrates emotion and cognition, helps direct the flow of energy.

As therapists, I believe that we work primarily with the mind and that the mind can affect and change the brain. Consider that when we ask clients to focus on their heart or when we hear them describe the fluttery feeling their anxious part is creating in their stomach, their PFC makes this possible. The mind is capable of shifting or changing states, and we rely on this in IFS when we ask a part to step back and separate or to shift from one state (or part) to another. The imagination is also in the mind and is known to be a powerful agent that promotes neuroplasticity (Doidge, 2007).

Norman Doidge and others first helped us understand that the brain can change via its capacity for *neuroplasticity*. When I went to medical school in the mid-1980s, this information was not yet known. Each time we have an experience, neurons fire in the brain, and this firing strengthens and grows new neural synapses (Doidge, 2007). We also know that we're capable of growing new nerve cells through a process known as *neurogenesis*. When the nervous system is working smoothly or harmoniously, Dan Siegel calls this *neural integration* and says it's the basis of healthy self-regulation (Siegel, 2017). This is what I like to refer to as mental health.

As the mind is related to function, the brain is related to structure. Different from the imagination and the mind, the brain consists of nerve cells, dendrites (the projections off the nerve cells), synapses (the space between nerve cells), and neurotransmitters (the chemicals that help nerve cells communicate with each other). It's also important to remember that the nervous system is not only located in the brain; it's everywhere throughout the body.

The brain alone has over 85 billion neurons, 100 trillion synapses, and 100 chemical neural transmitters. To put this in perspective, psychiatric medications primarily work on five of these chemical neural transmitters: dopamine, norepinephrine, serotonin, glutamate, and gamma-aminobutyric acid (GABA).

NEURONS TO NETWORKS TO PARTS

We know that a series of neurons string together to form what is called a *neural network*. Neural networks communicate with one another throughout the brain to give rise to thoughts, feelings, physical sensations, and complex actions.

One particular network that is relevant for clients with trauma histories is the vertical network or, as some refer to it, the top-down/bottom-up network. This network takes input from the body and brings it up into the brain, where it integrates emotional, cognitive, and physical information. Next, it travels to the PFC, which integrates and processes the information before it determines the appropriate response. This information is then brought back down to the body. Here is a diagram of the vertical network. We will revisit this network when we discuss the neurobiology of PTSD.

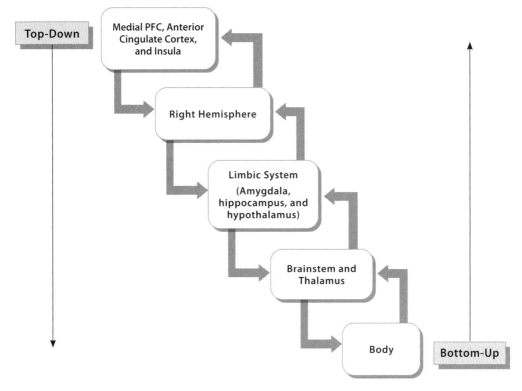

Trauma networks can be powerful and potent, holding very strong views, perceptions, and emotions. Louis Cozolino says that the vast majority of the input to the cortex comes from what is already inside our brain. We scan for examples that prove our preexisting beliefs, which are primarily driven by fear to avoid danger (Cozolino, 2010). This speaks to the experience I have when I'm working with clients who are in their trauma and they interpret what is happening in the present through the lens of their past. In contrast to "seeing things through rose-colored glasses," it's more like "seeing the world through trauma-colored glasses."

As mentioned earlier, it is beneficial for therapists to acknowledge and validate this trauma distortion, which increases the likelihood of it softening. I often use the following phrase from Brené Brown when talking to clients who are working through past experiences: "What's the story you're telling yourself right now?" This is a non-shaming way to ask about their parts' perceptions of the past that are currently being projected onto the present situation. These stories or internalized beliefs and feelings are potent, tenacious, and overpowering and have a formidable influence over our clients and their often-distorted view of the world.

A few years back, I experienced the power of distortion from my younger parts and the influence they had had on my present-day life. At the time, my father-in-law was sick, and my husband asked if he could visit him alone to spend some one-on-one quality time with him. This certainly seemed like a reasonable request to me, so I said of course. While my husband was away, I learned that the trip had morphed into a mini-family reunion. I began to experience, as they say, FOMO (fear of missing out).

As the days progressed, I also became aware of my younger parts and their feelings of being alone, abandoned, and increasingly desperate for connection. At the same time, I was aware of an angry part of me that was escalating. I began distancing myself from my partner in the service of protecting my younger parts from feeling more distressed and alone. It was utterly strange to be able to hold the present-day perspective, as well as feel both angry, hurt, and abandoned in connection to my past. I believe I was fortunate to have enough Self-energy present to witness all of this unfold within myself, which was a new experience for me.

I recognized how my angry part felt compelled to disconnect from my husband, and I identified how this angry part was trying to help my younger self. I also clearly saw how my angry part was perpetuating the problem. The angrier it got, the more it disconnected me from my husband; consequently, the lonelier and more abandoned my younger part felt.

My Self took charge and was able to reach out to my husband and be vulnerable with him. I asked my husband for help, who responded lovingly and caringly. Being able to experience all these emotions and be present in these feelings, both past and present, allowed me to subsequently heal my young attachment wound in the course of my own therapy, which has had an enormously positive impact on my life.

Being able to experience the desperation of the wounded part and the tenacity of the protective part, while simultaneously witnessing how they unintentionally worsened the problem, was enormously valuable for me on a personal and professional level. I have a new level of appreciation for the power of traumatic distortion and the IFS phrase "protectors draw to themselves the very thing they're protecting." I experienced this dynamic firsthand, and now I'm better able to stay present with myself and with my clients when we're blended, possessing a new level of appreciation as a result of this experience.

Protective parts come in a range of intensities and roles. What they all have in common is the desire and intention to keep the pain away in the service of self-preservation. *I speculate that parts live in the mind and that they utilize neural networks in the brain to express themselves.* I believe that protective parts, in particular, utilize unintegrated or dysregulated neural networks in the brain to express themselves. The parts that are not involved in protection or don't carry wounds utilize integrated neural networks in the brain to express themselves.

Going Inside

The process of *going inside* is not an easy one for many trauma survivors. First, most clients are used to traditional talk therapy, which primarily engages a storytelling part of the client. They need to adjust and become comfortable with focusing their attention internally versus externally. Second, the practice of going inside connects clients to their feelings and body sensations, which can be extremely uncomfortable for them because that's often where traumatic experiences are held.

In my experience, the transition of going inside is more difficult for clients than accepting the notion that they have parts. Most people spend much of their time getting away from their Self and inner experiences. Here, we're asking them to move toward their parts—to connect and listen to what's going on inside without necessarily talking or thinking about it. We're encouraging them to slow things down, turn inward, and get curious about what's going on inside.

Some protective parts that are vague, distracting, disconnected, and avoidant of the pain will naturally emerge because focusing intently on the problem makes them nervous. Other protective parts will take over, flood the system, and overwhelm the client with excessive emotion in an unsuccessful attempt to be heard and helped. I've noticed that with clients who tend to become overwhelmed, I can spend an inordinate amount of time helping them try to achieve *a healthy distance and perspective* from their feelings. However, with other clients—especially those who are numb and cut off—I frequently suggest they go inside and try to *move closer to and connect with* what they're feeling.

Both types of clients, those who feel too much and those who feel too little, have difficulty making decisions for themselves because they're disconnected from their true Self and living life predominantly through their parts. Clients with DID can rapidly switch from one side to the other within seconds, being overwhelmed in one moment and not feeling much at all in the next.

When you participate in traditional talk therapy, you and your clients are primarily engaged in what's called *exteroceptive awareness.* You're both focusing your attention externally and primarily engaging your PFC (Seppala, 2012). When you ask your clients to go inside, you're requesting that they shift their attention internally and engage in what's called *interoceptive awareness.* This relies on the insula (which integrates body awareness and emotion) and posterior cingulate gyrus (which connects to awareness, memory, emotions, and the default mode network). Both structures link to the limbic system and brainstem (Seppala, 2012), which are connected to the aforementioned vertical (or trauma) network.

In other words, when we ask our clients to focus internally, we are having them focus on the actual neural networks affected by their trauma; when we engage with them in talk therapy, we're primarily having them engage the PFC. I'm not saying that you can't heal complex trauma with talk therapy. However, I think it might take longer since clients cannot directly access the structures affected by trauma like they can when they are interoceptively connected. Consider also that research shows internal attention has a greater influence over our sense of happiness (Seppala, 2012).

IFS utilizes meditative practices primarily to help clients access Self-energy and aid in the unblending process. Meditation should not be compared to psychotherapy, as it is not a therapy modality. But clients who meditate can spontaneously experience moments of healing while engaged in meditation. There are many different forms of meditation, of course. Some forms of meditation suggest moving away from thoughts, feelings, and actions, while others encourage connecting with thoughts, feelings, and actions that show up with loving kindness or what is referred to as "metta." The latter approach is what we encourage with our clients. Jon Kabat-Zinn espouses the notion that mindfulness meditation can help with the uncoupling of thoughts and symptoms from oneself (Kabat-Zinn, 2003), which is very much in line with the IFS perspective of unblending.

As I see it, we need to encourage clients to clear their minds, help their parts relax, and see if Self-energy will naturally show up. This is a way to slow down their systems enough to allow for the emergence of the Self. The goal here is to foster a trusting relationship between protective parts and the Self. For example, I will frequently say: "What does this anxious part of you need right now to be able to trust your Self a little more?" This approach uses mindfulness to foster separation, help the Self emerge, and develop a trusting relationship between parts and the Self.

Britta Hozel and colleagues have researched the brain regions affected by mindfulness meditation and have demonstrated that meditation decreases activation in the amygdala (assigns emotional significance to events) and increases activation in the PFC (integrates emotion and cognition), insula (incorporates body awareness), anterior and posterior cingulate cortex (impacts attention, memory, emotion, and self-identity), and temporal-parietal junction (also connected to self-identity; Hozel et al., 2010, 2011). Many of these brain changes associated with mindfulness meditation are corrective experiences that help reverse the impact of trauma. When clients focus their mental energy internally, they are more likely to connect to the brain structures that were affected by trauma and need healing.

How clients and therapists focus their energy can have a powerful effect on the healing process. I'm often amazed at how much longer it takes my clients to unburden their wounds during individual therapy sessions in my office compared to how much more quickly this can happen during a training demonstration—when dozens of attendees engage in sending healing energy toward a chosen volunteer. It's incredible! The cumulative effect of focused energy produced by a group of people toward an individual is extremely powerful.

Here's the bottom line: Meditation is a useful tool to help clients unblend and access Self-energy. It positively affects the structures in the brain most affected by trauma.

FLESH OUT AND SEPARATE

Identifying parts and achieving separation (unblending) are among the main goals of the first three steps of the 6 F's. However, these tasks are easier said than done with complex trauma survivors and can take many months to achieve in some cases. Open-ended inquisitive questions can help clients establish a relationship with the part instead of being blended "in" the part. Good examples include: "Does the part have a color associated with it?" or "Where is it located in your body?" or "Does it move around or have a shape associated with it?" or "Do you see it, hear it, or feel it?" If they can answer the question, it shows that they're not totally blended with the part.

Early on in treatment, many trauma clients are primarily *in* their parts most of the time, so having them relax or separate, even slightly, can be challenging. With severely traumatized clients, it's easy for therapists to get frustrated by the lack of progress. Often, parts don't know or trust the Self enough to separate from it. In addition, "Self-like" parts will frequently show up and try to move the process along. You may hear the client compliantly say things like: "Sure, the part said it's willing to step back" or "Yes, I feel compassionate toward it." This can be confusing because it sounds as if things are moving forward, yet no real progress or healing ever happens. When this occurs, therapists can get discouraged, give up on IFS altogether, and go back to their old way of working with clients.

These three initial unblending steps can be taxing. But I encourage therapists to be patient and make the necessary effort up front to gain real separation before proceeding with steps four, five, and six. It will save time down the road if the target part is truly willing to separate and genuinely grant permission to proceed.

Strangely enough, one of the ways to achieve separation is to briefly encourage blending. If your client is not on the severe end of the dissociative spectrum (as is the case with DID) and you encourage the part to take over and share what it's feeling with you, as therapist, then the client's Self will likely be listening in the background, hear what the part has to say, and often appreciate the role it's playing.

In my personal therapy, I learned that my system generally blends first before any separation is possible. My parts tend to quickly take over and need to be heard before they are willing to relax and connect with my Self. Initially, I would resist this because it was so overwhelming for certain parts of me when intense parts took over. But over time, I've learned that this is the best way for my parts to truly achieve separation. They needed to blend first and say their piece; then they are willing to soften.

As I look back on this now, I sense that many of my parts were on their own for so long that they didn't believe anyone could or would be there for them. I've become more comfortable with their need to express themselves in this way. My parts take over, say what they need to say, look up at me, and see that my Self is listening to them. Once this happens, they're willing to relax. Mine is a "being in/before being with" or "take over and talk first, then separate later" kind of system. Remember, each system or collection of parts is different, and parts are capable of separating when they're ready. It's our job as therapists to be open and flexible and to learn how each system within our clients operates.

CHAPTER 7

Step 4: Self-Energy and Gaining Access to Internal Wisdom

Once the target part and other parts of the system have been identified and are willing to separate (the primary goal of the first three steps), the fourth step is to help clients gain access to Self-energy. We inquire about the presence of the Self when we ask questions like: "How do you feel toward the part that is depressed?" We then aim for responses aligned with what embodies Self-energy, such as: "I'm finally open and really ready to listen," "I care deeply and want to help that part," or "I'm feeling a great deal of love and appreciation for the depressed part right now." We are looking for statements that exemplify the 8 C's of Self-energy: *curiosity, clarity, confidence, calm, compassion, courage, creativity, and connectedness.*

I appreciate the perspective of Gary Zukav, someone Oprah Winfrey admires, who authored *The Seat of the Soul.* Zukav believes that the soul comes from a higher-order logic that is meaningfully reflective and connects to our emotions and heart (Zukav, 2014). He states that *incomplete* parts of the soul make up our five-sensory personality, which connects to our intellect and understanding and originates in the mind. He also believes that every discrepancy between our conscious mind and emotions points directly to a splintered aspect of the soul that requires healing. I believe this is consistent with the IFS perspective—that Self = soul = heart = emotion and parts = personality = intellect = conscious mind—and that healing is required when these components are fractured or out of alignment. To become whole, Zukav says, our soul must balance its energy.

I experience the Self in three different ways. First, I feel a tingling or flow of energy throughout my whole body, with a particular concentration in my arms and legs. I believe this happens when I connect to the energy in nature or my surroundings. Second, I have what feels like a titanium core inside of me that is solid and unwavering. When connected to this space, I feel calm and powerful; no one can push my boundaries or persuade me from my center. And when I speak from this place, people (my children, in particular) listen. The third dimension of Self-energy for me is when I connect to that which is beyond us: the spiritual realm. When I'm in the spiritual realm, I feel that all is and will be okay—that I can let go and things will work out exactly as they're supposed to. I can let go and fully trust the greater good.

I encourage you to explore the different ways you experience Self-energy. Do you feel it in connection to your environment or nature? What do you feel in your body when you're in Self-energy? Do you connect with something spiritual and, if so, how do you experience that?"

Comparing Compassion and Empathy

As therapists, we know that there are different ways to *be with* our clients. At times, we can be fully engaged and present, and at other times we can be bored, distracted, or preoccupied. We can also feel triggered, totally overwhelmed, or overinvolved. Tania Singer, the head of the social neuroscience lab at the Max Planck Institute in Germany, and her group have been able to map out two important ways we can be with someone else. One is by having compassion; the other is by being empathetic. Singer defines compassion as a feeling of concern for the suffering of others, coupled with the motivation to help them (Singer & Klimecki, 2014). Neuroimaging studies show that compassion involves the care-seeking neural network, specifically the ventral striatum, pregenual anterior cingulate cortex, and medial orbitofrontal cortex. Empathy, on the other hand, is defined as resonating with others' suffering. It involves interoceptive awareness and consists of a neural network in the anterior insula and anterior midcingulate cortex. Singer's research shows that compassion is a sustainable state, although we can burn out from being too empathic for too long.

From the IFS perspective, I see compassion as an unblended state of "being with," which is more aligned with Self-energy. Empathy, on the other hand, is a blended state of "being in" our parts and is more aligned with protective parts and exiles. With compassion, we are there for the other person with some amount of distance, perspective, and a genuine desire to help them, which can be incredibly important and necessary, especially when a trauma survivor is overwhelmed and activated in the moment.

Compassion is useful for clients, as well as therapists, particularly during intense therapeutic moments, because it provides a sense of safety for all. I believe this aligns with the experience of Self-energy, which involves having presence and perspective while being open and available to help others. Parts of our clients will need and want this from us at times. *The energy of compassion is a positive force; it fosters trust and is, I believe, an antidote to fear.*

At other times, our clients or their parts will want us to truly "get" what they are feeling. Think of how many times you have heard: "How can you possibly help me? You have no idea what it's like to grow up with an alcoholic father and a verbally abusive mother?" or "You're so put together; your life is perfect." Here the client is saying: "I don't feel you empathically resonating with me right now." When we are able to resonate with someone else and with what they're feeling in the moment, I believe we're *not* actually feeling what they are experiencing at all. Instead, we're connected to and feeling *our own experience* while they're undergoing their experience. With empathy, our protectors or our wounds can get activated when we're working with a client who is "in" their experience or blended with their parts.

For example, I recently welled up with emotion when working with a client who was overwhelmed and vulnerable upon talking about the difficulty of parenting children when they're totally out of control. I relived my own intense experiences while she relived hers. With empathy, our parts get activated, and we blend with them as we resonate with our client's pain. We don't necessarily need to have the same experience as our client, but we need to relate to the *feelings* associated with their event. Empathy can help us connect with and relate to our clients. We have something in common and identify with their anguish as we connect with our own similar past experiences.

With compassion, our parts are not activated and we are not blended. Rather, we remain in a calm state, connected with the client's presence and capable of identifying their pain without getting overwhelmed by it. *Truly being present with our clients requires a delicate balance of being empathically resonant (being with our own parts) while not getting too overwhelmed by them, as well as having a compassionate distance and perspective without being too withdrawn or detached.*

My experience is that parts of our clients need and desire both empathy and compassion from the therapist at various times. These parts also need and require empathy and compassion from their Self too. (More on this later, when we explore healing wounds in chapter 23.) Empathy, when not overwhelming, can inform compassion. If I feel a bit of empathy, it can help me be present and emotionally engaged with my client while adopting a compassionate stance.

Too much empathy, however, can engulf us and block our ability to have the necessary distance and perspective to hold a compassionate position with our clients. Jen Kleiner, a friend and colleague of mine, reminded me that there are times when we can perceive the feelings of another person without necessarily feeling compassion for or empathizing with them. I agree with her; it is possible to sense another person's energy and emotions without activating our own feelings. This is what occurs with psychics and energy healers. They are trained to pick up and sense the feelings, thoughts, and beliefs in others.

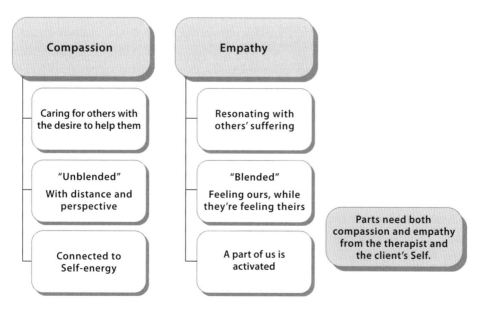

Many therapists, myself included, are what the general public refers to as an "empath." I grew up with people constantly saying to me: "You're too sensitive" and "You react so strongly to everything." I suspect these qualities identified by others relate to my natural temperament, as well as to my personal trauma history. It was common for me (although less so now after all the healing I've achieved) to be overwhelmed and drained after a full day of sitting with clients. I tended to take in and absorb what I heard, bringing these experiences and emotions home with me at the end of the day.

I suspect that many of us in the field are also "highly sensitive" people and magnets for other people's feelings. Being sensitive can certainly be a gift as well as a curse. Fortunately, I have gotten much better at clearing the energy I've experienced with one client before engaging with the next. This is a big reason why I'm a strong proponent of the 50-minute therapy session: Having at least 10 minutes between sessions allows me to wipe the slate clean and reenergize before welcoming the next client.

Empathy as a Part

I'll never forget the time my son was in the hospital after sustaining an injury from a mountain-biking accident. Visiting hours were coming to a close, and I wanted to stay with him overnight. I couldn't bear the idea of him being all alone in that hospital room. "Papa, you can go home—I'll be fine," he told me.

As I drove home, Dick Schwartz called me to check in and see how my son and I were doing. I broke out into tears, feeling completely overwhelmed by the events of the day as I tried to explain to him what was going on.

"Pull over. Let's see what's going on with your parts," Dick said.

My response was gruff and impatient: "Explore what's going on? Didn't you hear me? My son is in the hospital."

Dick's next few words took me by surprise. "I know, Frank, but let's see if the part of you that's so overwhelmed right now can separate and tell us more about what it's holding."

I parked on the side of the road, and we began to explore the overwhelmed part of me. Much to my surprise, I discovered that there was a wounded part of me overreacting to the thought of my son being alone and in pain. This part was rooted in me as a little boy, at a time when I was totally alone after being physically abused as a child. I recognized that this part had taken over and blocked my ability to be open, available, and loving toward my son. In retrospect, I think my son sensed this panicked feeling in me, which prompted him to tell me to go home and not worry.

In typical Dick Schwartz fashion, he helped me unburden that little boy inside me while I sat in my car on the side of the road. The next day, when I went in to visit my son, I apologized for overreacting the previous night. I found that I was now able to connect with him, not due to excessive empathy, but because I came from a more compassionate place of love, concern, and genuine curiosity for what he was going through. This became compassion informed by empathy. I was able to listen to my son's experience and share with him that I, too, have felt similar emotions.

I encourage you to explore and practice the differences between compassion (being with) and empathy (being in) as it relates to helping your clients. See if you can sense what compassion feels like internally and how your clients experience your compassionate presence. Then repeat the exercise by using empathy. What does it feel like for you to get emotional when you're sitting with someone? Does it make you feel uncomfortable? What are the origins of these feelings? Again, I believe parts need both empathy and compassion from us, as well as from our clients' Self. Being attuned to this balance, however, can be complicated. Try to determine what percentage of empathy (reliving) and compassion (being with) you need to give to your client's parts so that they can feel heard, seen, and known by you and the Self within them. This balance helps the client feel safe enough to reveal and release the pain they've been carrying.

ARE YOU BORN WITH IT, OR IS IT CULTIVATED?

Many, including me, equate the Self with the soul and believe it connects to a higher source (whatever that means to you personally or to your client). IFS espouses the idea that we're automatically born with this Self and that it doesn't need to be cultivated or developed (Schwartz & Sweezy, 2020). Dick Schwartz told me that the Self has an agenda—one of love and connection—but this agenda isn't attached to an outcome. The Self is like software that utilizes the hardware (our developing human body) to express itself, and it has more to work with as we grow and develop.

I experience a difference between the *human* embodiment of Self-energy compared to a *spiritual* experience of the Self. For example, my human Self is singular, and it has a gender and sexual orientation. My spiritual Self, on the other hand, which I experience at various times in my life, connects to the oneness that is all around and within us and doesn't seem to possess a gender or an orientation.

I believe Self-energy is a "state of being" that lives in the mind and utilizes integrated neural networks in the brain to express itself. The Self connects to our internal energy, as well as the external energy found in our environment. I experience the Self as a maximally integrative state in which all is connected and flows together in unison.

When Tania Singer and I were discussing the neuroscience origins of Self-energy, she mentioned to me that she wondered if it was the *absence* of neural network firing that was connected to the state of Self-energy. She noticed that when she scanned the brains of very experienced meditators, their brains were quickly able to turn off and enter a state of no neuronal activation. This is an interesting idea I hope we'll get more clarity on with further research.

One thing I consistently see is that clients with extreme and extensive trauma histories, such as severe neglect or DID, tend to take months to years to be able to access Self-energy. It can take extended lengths of time for protective parts to get to know and trust the Self enough to relax and allow it to emerge naturally. When we work with protective parts that begin to feel seen and known, I believe they allow us to *access* the Self that's already there. I contend that there's no need to cultivate the

Self; instead, recognizing and accepting parts helps to *cultivate access to the Self.* I see the Self as the capable, competent leader that's naturally within all of us.

The Self versus Self-Like Parts

During a particularly poignant session with Mia, a client of mine who carries a diagnosis of DID, one of her Self-like parts shared an important perspective with me about the relationship between her Self and her parts. Mia's Self-like part started explaining to me how these parts worked. She said: "I have to tell you, Frank, I know the Self has good intentions, but it scares some of these parts. They feel like the Self is trying to replace them. They're trying so hard to erase the past and never let it surface again. And sometimes, they feel upset with the Self because it seems okay being with all the bad stuff that happened in the past. It's going to take these parts some time to get used to the Self in a way that doesn't feel threatening to them and their stories. Remember, parts hold most of the real estate in here, and they feel like the Self is invading their turf."

As Mia's therapy continued, her revelations became more surprising: "The Self keeps challenging the parts' views. It makes some of the parts feel like they're wrong for feeling, believing, and responding the way that they do, even though the Self does so in a gentle way. Some of the parts feel threatened by the Self. Last week, for example, the Self expressed another way to handle Jenna when she ghosted us. The suicidal part felt judged and took offense to that comment, and the little one felt shamed. When the Self makes a suggestion like that, some of the parts feel defensive, inadequate, or bad about themselves. Remember, these parts are pretty young. We have to move really slowly to build trust in these relationships. I hope you can understand all of this, Frank."

I told her Self-like part that I understood completely and was grateful for her willingness to share this important perspective with me. "Thank you," I said.

"You're welcome," Mia's part replied. "I felt that it needed to be said."

Hearing this perspective from Mia's Self-like part helped me and my parts relax. It made me refrain from trying so hard to get her parts to acquiesce in an effort to help her Self come forward. Mia's Self-like part gave me a birds-eye view of the fascinating world of our parts. It fostered a deeper respect for and understanding of these parts and their pace.

So how do you differentiate between the Self and Self-like parts? For me, it has to do with energy—a state of being in which I can distinguish between the two. *The Self is energy-expanding, while Self-like parts with agendas tend to be more energy-constricting.* The Self has a calm power associated with it, and it taps into something greater. Self-like parts have useful energy, which understands, does, and says the right thing and helps figure things out. It's smaller and more localized.

THE SELF AND TRAUMA

What happens to Self-energy during a trauma? Does it stay and endure the unspeakable? Does it leave? Do parts jump in and take over? This is a long-standing debate within the IFS community. I've spent a fair about of time thinking about this question and have discussed it with Dick Schwartz to make sure my thinking aligns with his.

I believe the Self is preserved and protected from trauma, and there is a resultant chasm created between the Self and parts as a result of overwhelming life experiences. Where the Self goes during a trauma is unclear. Some clients describe the Self as leaving the body, while others feel it remains present but out of harm's way. Whatever the case, parts often hold the experience that the Self has left them behind to endure the painful experience. Luckily, IFS has a way of repairing the relational breach created between the Self and parts as a result of a violation, which we'll discuss in chapter 9.

It's also possible for a fraction of the Self to be split off or exiled in severe trauma. It doesn't get damaged or sustain a burden per se, but a portion of it can be left behind or remain in the past, while the remainder of the Self moves forward in life. During a particularly intense unburdening of mine, I was surprised to encounter a younger aspect of my Self (not a wounded part) that was stuck in the past. It said: "I'm still here. I've always been here. No one ever saw me [meaning my parents]." There was a beautifully poignant reunion or integration between the portion of my Self that remained in the past and my Self of today. I was so surprised by this experience that I quickly called Dick to make sure this was consistent with IFS and his understanding of the Self. He said it was. A portion of the Self can sometimes get exiled during extreme trauma.

I also believe the opposite is true too: *Self-energy, or love, is the antidote to trauma.* Self-energy has the infinite capacity to *be with* and heal trauma. We see this over and over again during the unburdening process. The Self doesn't directly experience, support, or condone abuse within us or others; it overcomes and rises above it. This is one of the great gifts of IFS, the healing capacity of the Self. In other words, in its most basic form, love heals trauma. Love, in fact, conquers trauma.

I have certainly heard parts say things like: "You left me to be raped by Uncle John." Here, parts relay the experience that the Self has left them behind to endure the abuse. I have also heard parts say: "I have to drink. It's my job. It's what I've always known. I have to show up and stop the pain." In this scenario, parts believe it's their role to serve and protect the Self during and after the trauma. I've heard the Self say: "I was up in the corner of the bedroom looking at that sweet little girl being hurt by Uncle John." Here the Self describes leaving during an overwhelming event. I have also heard the Self describe being hijacked by triggered parts: "The anxious part keeps jumping in and taking over" or "Someone just took me out right there."

I believe all of the following are true. *Our essence or our soul is protected from trauma. Parts are left behind, feel abandoned by the Self, and are forced to endure the pain and nightmare of the trauma. And when wounds are triggered, protective parts will jump in and take over the Self in the service of protection.*

Remember, it is common for parts to be angry with the Self for abandoning it during the trauma. These parts often have no real interest in connecting with the Self. Dick Schwartz mentioned to me that clients with DID commonly have parts that *hate* the presence of Self-energy because, historically, perpetrators have attacked it whenever it was present. Hence, when the Self shows up, clients can have parts that get scared and are afraid of perpetrator retribution.

With many trauma clients, we look for what *percentage of the client's Self* is present at any given moment. We know that each time a part feels seen, heard, and validated, it relaxes a bit further and more Self-energy is accessible in their system. Be aware that this can take a long time with your more severely traumatized clients. Their parts have been "running the show" for many years, and they're used to being in charge and making decisions for the system.

Case in point: June, one of my more dissociative clients, shared a beautiful and clear example of this very dilemma during a therapy session. She said: "I am the Self, and I'm truly sorry that, during the abuse, I left the body behind. It was reflexive, my essence came with me, and the body mass was left behind. There are other times, when the voices get so intense and jump in and take over. They can be really powerful sometimes. It's hard for me to stay during those times because they're so strong when they get triggered."

Anthony, a different client, shared: "Any expression of the Self was dangerous for me as a child. If I were honest and spoke truthfully about what my father did to me, I would have gotten killed. Expressing my love of art and music would have only caused the bullies at school to attack me more. There really wasn't room for my Self and my parts to coexist back then."

Another client described her experience of the Self as follows: "It's impervious. It's impenetrable. When I'm in alignment, I have mine and they have theirs. It's clear; it's the end of the story. On the other hand, when I'm out of alignment, I'm trying to be what other people want me to be, or I'm trying to give them what they need from me. I'm beginning to believe there's a connection between my being out of alignment and all of my medical issues."

I certainly know this to be true for me personally. I grew up responding to what other people needed and wanted of me in the service of self-survival. I'm now aware that when my asthma flares up, for instance, it's a sign that I'm out of alignment, that I'm disconnected from my truth and from what feels right for me. Sometimes it can take me a while to fully listen to the message that this part (that is, the part that expresses itself through my asthma) is trying to communicate with me. But when I can reconnect and freely feel and speak to the truth in my life, my asthma typically resolves.

Pain and trauma are a normal part of our *human* experience here on Earth, and the aspect of us that comes from the source (i.e., the divine) is protected and doesn't suffer or sustain trauma. Unfortunately, parts of us are left behind to do the heroic job of enduring the trauma, protecting the exiled parts of us that hold the pain, and ultimately preserving the goodness and purity within us that is our Self. In this view, evil does not win over goodness.

THE CONTAINER THEORY

As we've discussed, the Self is preserved during overwhelming experiences, and protective parts are forced to take on extreme roles within the system to protect and fend off the resultant heartache. It's almost as if each person or human body has a *finite amount of space* within itself, and when most of the space inside is taken up by numerous protective parts and several wounded exiles, there is, by default, very little residual space for the Self to occupy.

I call this the *container theory*. How much space do parts take up, and how much space is available for the Self? In severe trauma, the urgency and necessity for protection require that most of the space in the container be consumed by intense and energetically large protective parts—thus leaving little available room for the Self. Let's say that protective parts and exiles collectively occupy 85 percent of the container; that means only 15 percent remains for the Self. With these clients, I intermittently observe the Self emerging. I know it's in there, but there's not a lot of space for it, and it doesn't have the opportunity to show itself very often due to the dominance of space-occupying parts.

However, as we gradually get to know the players in the system, and they begin to trust us and the client's Self more, these hardworking protective parts tend to relax, and the Self emerges more often. In my experience, this is a slow process that requires an enormous amount of patience by even the most skilled therapist.

Again, to what degree does the Self actually leave? To what extent are parts so numerous and active that there's not enough space left for the Self? I don't have definitive answers to these questions. But I'll continue to remain observant and listen to what my clients' parts and their Self tell me about these various scenarios. By staying in the conversation and trusting the process, I'm certain we'll get more clarity over time.

We're all a combination of the Self and parts, and it's the flow between them that brings us into balance and harmony. Trauma disrupts this balance because parts are forced to carry the pain or to work extremely hard to keep the wounds at bay. This burns an enormous amount of energy and occupies lots of space within the container. When we help parts release what they're forced to do or carry, there will be a greater percentage in the container that the Self can occupy.

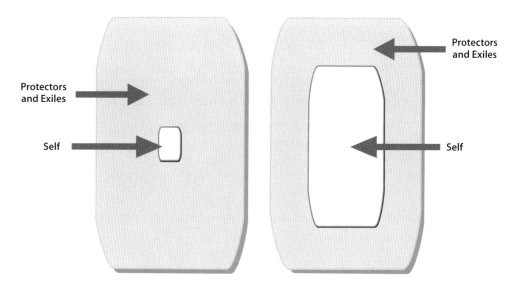

CHAPTER 8

Steps 5 and 6: BeFriending, Finding the Job, and Finding the Fear

IFS as Internal Attachment Work

Once the target part has separated from the client's Self, and the Self is accessible and connected to the part, it's time to begin fostering an internal relationship between them. Remember that there was a chasm created between them as a result of a relational violation once upon a time. Now we're ready to repair that connection. There is a back-and-forth process that is important and often overlooked by therapists at this stage, as demonstrated in the following hypothetical therapist-client dialogue:

> "Nancy, how do you feel toward the part that eats in excess now?" the therapist asks.

> "I really care about her and see that she's just a little girl who's been holding so much for so long," Nancy says.

> "Send her that caring energy right now, Nancy, and see if she's willing to take it in," the therapist suggests.

Often, therapists identify Self-energy in their clients and feel like they're good to go. But that's only half of the story. We want to make sure that this is a two-way street by asking questions like: "How do you feel toward her (Self-to-part connection)? Is she willing or able to take that in (part-to-Self connection)?" Often, parts aren't willing or ready to accept positive Self-energy. They either don't trust the Self yet or are in a relationship with a Self of the past. (More on this to come in chapter 9.)

Helping clients foster this internal relationship between their target part and the Self is something that takes time, especially in relational trauma, but allowing it to develop slowly over time will pay off in the long run. Be aware that this is new for the part—to have someone who cares for it and genuinely wants to help it. Just as you'd gradually introduce a stray cat into your home as a pet, it's important to proceed gingerly and allow the relationship to deepen over time.

LEARN ABOUT THE POSITIVE INTENTIONS

Once the relationship between the Self and the part feels somewhat secure, we proceed with helping the client learn the part's job or role. Think of this as the beginning of a friendly interview. Ask questions such as: "What's your primary goal for Nancy? How long have you been helping her in this way? How effective do you feel in this role?" It's important for you and the client to learn about the part's intentions from its perspective or point of view. *Once you both genuinely comprehend and acknowledge the positive objectives of a protective part, a natural relationship and compassionate stance toward that part can develop.* Engage in affirming dialogue, like: "Of course, it makes sense that you found eating as a way to keep the depression at bay. I get why you feel the need to do that. Nancy, are you hearing this? How are you feeling toward this part now, after you've heard how it's trying to help?"

Ideally, Nancy would respond in a similar fashion: "I had no idea that the eating part was trying to help me not feel so depressed and lonely. I know my childhood was really awful at times. I'm appreciative of her and really admire her effort."

To which, you'd say: "Let her know that now, Nancy, and see how she responds."

If Nancy says something like, "She is loving that," you know a two-way connection has been established.

Understanding the positive intention of protective parts opens the door to repairing the internal chasm that occurred during the original assault. I'm always looking for that heart-opening experience within myself and within my client. It's an important first step in gaining permission from the part to access the wound. Genuine permission occurs with a heartfelt awareness of the part's true intention. *Learning about the positive intention is learning about its job.* Once the job is revealed, it's a good idea to ask the part what else it wants to share, as feeling heard, known, and seen goes a long way toward getting permission to access the wounds it protects.

FOCUSING ON FEAR: EXILES REVEALED

Once you and your client have aligned with the positive intention of the protective part, it's essential to learn about its fear. Ask the client's part this crucial question: *"What are you afraid would happen if you didn't do this job?"* As many of you have learned from your Level 1 training, this question will either reveal the exile that the protective part is protecting or reveal a different part within the client's system that is polarized from (or in conflict with) the protector on which you're focusing. The client may say: "If I stop drinking, James (another protective part) will get suicidal" or "If I stop drinking, James will see how alone he is in the world (an exile)." Try not to get frustrated if this question doesn't reveal either of these responses. Remember that protective parts are good at being protective; they don't like to reveal important or vulnerable information so easily. In these circumstances, asking the "And then what?" question is often helpful. This is particularly useful with hypoaroused parts or more blunted systems that tend to respond with one- or two-word answers. Here's a constructive therapist-client dialogue to expound on this point:

"Jay, what is this part afraid will happen if it isn't anxious any longer?"

"That would be unknown," Jay says.

"And what is scary about the unknown?"

"We would lose control," Jay says.

"And what if you lost control?" the therapist asks.

"We don't like feeling out of control."

"What would be the worst-case scenario if you did feel out of control?"

"Oh no, we won't ever do that again."

"So let me see if I get this right: You're fearful of letting go of the anxiety because you're afraid of feeling those same out-of-control emotions you felt as a little boy when you were bullied at school? Is that right, Jay?"

"Yes, exactly," he says.

In this example, using the what-if question reveals the exile (feeling out-of-control emotions during abuse) underneath the protector (the anxious part).

ADDRESSING PROTECTOR FEARS

A common frustration and one of the biggest roadblocks for therapists new to IFS is addressing protector fears. It's common to get stuck, not know what to ask next, give up, and resort to your familiar way of providing therapy. For nearly 35 years, Dick Schwartz has been addressing protector fears with clients. I often watch him at work with amazement, realizing how masterful and efficient he is at convincing protectors to relax.

Addressing protector fears is one of those steps in the IFS model that takes practice, trial-and-error tenacity, and patience. The chart on the next page provides a list of common protector fears, along with some common responses. I've expanded this list from the *IFS Skills Training Manual* (Anderson et al., 2017) because I've become aware—with the help of Fran Booth, an assistant trainer at the IFS Institute—that there are two important components to addressing protector fears: The first is making sure the part feels heard and understood by validating its job and its fear. The second is offering clients an alternative solution to their problem.

Addressing protector fears is something that takes time and practice. At times, you'll be encouraging your client to have these discussions with their part (which IFS calls *insight*). Other times, when there isn't Self-energy present in your client, you can talk directly to the part (called *direct access*, which we'll discuss in chapter 9) in the hopes of getting the part to separate and grant permission to proceed.

Protector Fear	Common Responses
"I'm afraid he'll be overwhelmed by the terror." (The most common protector fear in trauma)	• *Validate*: "I totally get that you're afraid Steve will be overwhelmed by the amount of pain and terror that's in there. That makes sense." • *Alternative solution*: "What if I were able to guarantee you that the part holding the terror won't overwhelm him? I'm not interested in anyone in there reliving what they went through. There's a different way to do this—by having the parts share a little bit at a time. Are you interested in that?" (See how to deal with overwhelm in chapter 9.)
"If I step back, then what will I do? This is what I've always done."	• *Validate*: "I hear that you're afraid of losing your job. Is that correct?" • *Alternative solution*: "We are not interested in getting rid of you in any way. But we can help you no longer feel anxious all the time. What if you were freed up to do something else? Are you interested in that?"
"If I step back, the suicidal part will take over."	• *Validate*: "I hear that you're afraid that another part will take over if you step back. That's a legitimate fear; it has happened before." • *Alternative solution*: "I don't want any part to feel the need to take over. We're going to listen to all parts and only move forward when they've all been heard and permit us to proceed, including the suicidal part."
"If you know me and what I've done, you'll hate me."	• *Validate*: "It sounds like you're afraid that I or Steve's Self might judge you if we get to know you better and learn more about what you needed to do to protect his little boy. Is that correct?" • *Alternative solution*: "I can assure you that I don't feel any judgment toward you at all. I know that you've tried your best to protect little Steve. If you ever see or feel me judging you in any way, please let me know. Are you willing to do that?"
"If anyone ever finds out what my dad did to me, my family would never talk to me again."	• *Validate*: "I hear that you're afraid of exposing this secret and that if your family found out, they would reject you. Is that right?" • *Alternative solution*: "If you permit us to heal the wound, you'll have the choice to tell whomever you want to tell. It will be your decision."
"You can't handle my pain."	• *Validate*: "I'm hearing that you're worried about my ability to cope with and process what happened to you. Is there anything I've said or done to give you that impression? Or are you just afraid this might be the case?" • *Alternative solution*: "I've been doing this work for a long time now. If you ever perceive anything that makes you suspicious of my ability to be with your feelings, please let me know. I also want to let you know that we're going to heal the pain so you will no longer need to feel it yourself. How does that sound to you?"
"If I get better, we won't work together anymore."	• *Validate*: "I hear that you're afraid of losing a connection with me if you get better. • *Alternative solution*: "You can choose how long you want to stay in treatment with me. I also know that when the wound heals, your younger parts will feel safely connected to you and won't feel the need for my help in the same way that they do right now. Does that make sense to you?"
"Every time things get better or I feel happy, something terrible happens."	• *Validate*: "I'm hearing that feeling good is scary. Is there anything else you want to share with me, or do I fully grasp your concern?" • *Alternative solution*: "What if there was a way for you to let go of that anticipatory fear? What if you could trust that Steve would be able to handle whatever came up, both the good and the bad, and you didn't have to be involved in his current life anymore? Are you interested in that option?
"This Self you keep referring to doesn't exist in me. I'm the exception to the rule. We (Steve's parts) handle everything for him, and we've been doing that his whole life."	• *Validate*: "I get that you've needed to handle everything for Steve up to this point. I also understand that he hasn't shown up much and that you don't even believe Steve exists in the way that I describe him. Is that correct?" • *Alternative solution*: "What if I could show you there's a place within that can handle all the pain you went through? Would you be interested in that? It would require all of you to step back for that to happen. All I'm asking for is a few moments. Are you willing to try? I know this is a big ask, and I understand if you're not willing to try it. It's your decision."

CHAPTER 9

Beyond the 6 F's for Trauma

One of the main reasons why treating trauma survivors is so stressful is because of the intensity, persistence, and extreme nature of traumatic symptoms, which IFS refers to as "parts." As mentioned earlier, the 6 F's are the main steps we move through when encountering protective parts. Our goals are to identify these parts, to gain access to Self-energy, to learn about the parts' jobs and fears, and to reveal who they're protecting. Often, these steps aren't enough to gain full permission to access the wounds that tenacious protective parts are keeping at bay. Additional steps I've found to help gain approval from protective parts associated with trauma follow next. I call these extra steps *Beyond the 6 F's*.

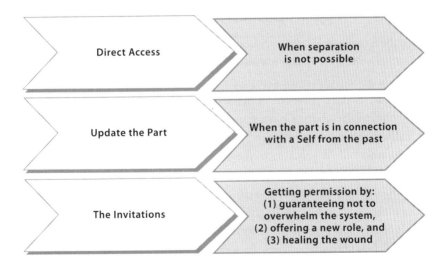

DIRECT ACCESS

Another great IFS contribution to the treatment of complex trauma is *direct access* or when a therapist's Self talks directly to the client's part (Schwartz & Sweezy, 2020). Direct access is an essential skill to master, especially when your client is blended with their part or has little or no access to Self-energy. When traumatized clients are triggered, parts can range from physiologically activated or sympathetically hyperaroused to blunted or parasympathetically hypoaroused.

When these extreme parts take over clients, their physiology is dominated by these intense states, and there is little or no access to the Self in those moments. Their greatest chance to unblend or separate from these severe states is for the therapist's Self to talk directly to the part that has temporarily taken over. This, of course, is contingent on the therapist's capacity to invoke their Self without being overtaken by one of their own parts in response to the client's intensity.

All therapists can benefit from being proficient at direct access and capable of fluidly moving in and out of this mode as if it were second nature, especially with more severely traumatized clients. Using direct access provides a quick and efficient way to overcome the reluctance and stubborn nature of many protective parts that are unwilling to budge. It certainly takes some getting used to, and it can feel a bit strange when you first incorporate it into your practice.

Direct access is one of the first tools I teach during IFS Level 2 trauma training. Many therapists have heard about it in their Level 1 training, but in my experience, few therapists are truly comfortable with using it routinely in their clinical practice. I encourage everyone who works with complex PTSD clients to regularly incorporate direct access into their repertoire of resources. I am confident it will help move treatment forward and enable your clients to more quickly unblend from their entrenched, persistent, and severe parts.

IMPLICIT VERSUS EXPLICIT DIRECT ACCESS

There are two different types of direct access: implicit and explicit (Schwartz & Sweezy, 2020). *Explicit direct access* is when you directly name and address the part aloud and engage it in a conversation. For example, you might say: "So you're the part of Noah that eats in excess, is that correct?" This is in contrast to *implicit direct access*, where the therapist talks to the client's part(s) in an indirect, general, or passive way without specifically calling them out as a "part." For instance: "I sense that you're feeling angry and upset right now" or "I want to make sure everyone feels safe before we proceed."

I use both implicit and explicit direct access, but I'm a bigger fan of the latter, especially when it comes to working with traumatized parts. They can often take over, dominate the client's system, rapidly switch from one part to another, or feel as if they are the actual client. You might, for example, get a response like: "Why do you call me 'a part of Noah'? I *am* Noah."

When such a scenario occurs, I don't spend too much time trying to encourage the part to separate from the client's Self. I may ask once or twice, but if I'm not successful, I move quickly into direct access. Parts will often prefer to talk to me over the client anyway. From the parts' perspective, I haven't abandoned them during the time of the trauma, and they are often curious to get to know me better—to see for themselves if I'm safe and trustworthy. I tend to utilize implicit direct access earlier on in treatment as I'm getting familiar with the client's system. I talk in general terms to a collective of parts. For example: "I know there's a lot of you in there who are hurting right now, and I want to let you know that relief is on the way."

The main goal of direct access is to help entrenched parts separate from the Self. Remember that they may also be interested in getting to know you better, but be careful not to form individual or special relationships with any parts. This could quickly turn dangerous and be experienced as a reenactment for some parts, as this is a common dilemma in some relational violations that incorporated "special" or "secret" relationships.

I always make a habit of sharing with the whole system what I've learned from the part during direct access. If the client doesn't have DID, they're usually listening in the background to what their blended part and I are discussing. But clients with DID often are not present or listening, or they don't want to hear what the part and I are talking about. I'll usually share with my client what I've learned from their part because I don't want to perpetuate any secrets or forge separate relationships with any of my client's parts. Complex PTSD often involves secrets and hidden relationships that can be quite damaging, and I'm not interested in contributing to that cycle in any way.

Remember that parts know how to write emails and send voice messages too. So be mindful of who's communicating what, and make sure you don't inadvertently participate in a reenactment.

I typically continue engaging the part in a conversation until it believes that I fully get its role, concern, and fear, as well as anything else it wants me to know. The part will likely be much more willing to step back when it feels fully heard, seen, and validated.

Here is an example of therapist-client dialogue involving explicit direct access, which shows the type of information that can be learned by talking directly to the part:

"So you're the part of Sue that's anxious, is that correct?" asks the therapist.

"I'm myself, and I'm anxious," responds Sue's part.

"Yes, I know. Tell me more about your anxiety."

"It's really crippling. Sometimes I can hardly function, and I get stomachaches and have trouble breathing."

"That sounds really awful. How long has this been going on for you?"

"Ever since the cancer diagnosis last September. It's unbearable to imagine my kids growing up without their mother."

"Well, that certainly makes a lot of sense to me. What else do you want to share with me? I want to make sure I get all that you're holding."

After the part has shared all that it's carrying and feels 100 percent heard, the therapist invites Sue's Self to join the conversation.

"Can you bring Sue back? I want to make sure she heard all of that."

"I didn't realize how hard my anxiety was working on my kids' and my behalf. I also heard how tired it was."

"Great, Sue. Let the anxious part know that you understand the ways it's trying to help and how tired it is. Let it know that we can help, if it's interested."

"I'm suddenly feeling calmer as you say that."

UPDATE AND APOLOGY

Once separation has occurred between the Self and the part and you begin fostering an internal relationship between them, one of the big challenges in working with relational trauma is ensuring that the target part is in connection with the *current-day* Self. This is the second step in Beyond the 6 F's that, if forgotten or overlooked, can cause frustration and confusion within the therapist because, despite moving through the steps of the IFS protocol, no real progress occurs.

The Self is in connection with the part, which typically happens first, but the part is often stuck in the past at the time of the trauma. It may not be the exact moment of the traumatic event. However, at some point around the time the trauma occurred, there was a split between the part that endured the event and the client's Self. The overwhelming nature of trauma caused this chasm. *The target part is often still in relationship with and has feelings toward the Self of the past.*

Here is an example of therapist-client dialogue in which an attempt to update the part is made:

> "Amir, can you send your worried part the love that you're feeling for it right now and see if it's willing to take that in?"

> "It doesn't want my love. It's looking away."

Note that anytime a part is unwilling to accept positive regard from the Self, it's a sign that it's in relationship to a Self of the past.

> "Amir, can you ask your worried part how old it thinks you are? And just say the first thing that comes to mind. Don't filter your answer."

Often, the client will disregard what it hears at first, believing that it isn't possible that the part still sees the client at that age.

> "Wow—I hear my part say age 12. That's crazy."

> "Let him see that you're no longer 12, Amir."

Here, we look for any words that elicit Self-energy, like "your core," "your inner wisdom," or "the you that's not a part." Be careful not to say "your adult self," as this can address a high-functioning manager part.

> "He can't believe how old I am. He had no idea I actually grew up."

> "Just give him some time to get to know the openhearted you. Ask him what he needs to be able to trust you now."

A part is typically not aware that the Self has continued to progress beyond the trauma, and they're not particularly interested in connecting with the current-day Self much anyway. That's because a part feels resentful for being left behind to suffer the consequences of the abuse. From the part's perspective, the Self deserted it.

In more severe forms of trauma, like DID and attachment trauma, parts initially often hate the Self for this abandonment. The Self, in turn, is marginally accessible, inconsistently shows up, and has a hard time reliably committing to the part. Parts are well aware of this and therefore hesitant to connect with the Self of today until the relationship feels safe and dependable. Here, therapists should take the time to cultivate this connection between the current-day Self and the target part because once this relationship is secure, gaining permission to access the wound is much easier.

We assist in repairing the chasm that occurred between the part and the Self of the past by introducing the part to the Self of today and supporting the newfound connection between them. *It's important for the current-day Self to apologize for this breach (even though it didn't occur intentionally) and for not being able to protect the part in the way that it needed and wanted back then.*

After the part is introduced to the Self of today, I frequently will ask the client's Self if there is anything it would like to say to that younger part now. When the Self is fully present, I'll typically hear things like: "I'm so sorry I wasn't there for you in the way that you needed me to be. I was 10 years old also, and I did the best I could. I'm truly sorry." This kind of response is a useful barometer of Self-energy because when there isn't enough Self-energy around, these apologies can feel hollow and inauthentic. When the Self is present, it's heartfelt.

Case in point: An adult client named Maya was raped by a group of teenage boys when she was 8 years old. She described how her parts felt the need to come in and rescue her younger Self:

> "She couldn't protect herself, so we had to jump in and save her," one of Maya's protective parts said during a session.

> Maya's current-day Self responded: "My parts don't trust me. I let them down back then. I couldn't handle what happened to us, and I really feel sorry about that now. I remember feeling defeated and all alone. Nobody in my family ever asked me what happened that day. They knew something bad went down, but no one cared enough to ask me anything about it."

Maya described how her protective parts carry the burden of believing they needed to protect the Self back then and how her current-day Self feels sorry about not being strong enough to endure the abuse. Her protective parts bear the burden of the trauma, and her Self holds the regret about not being able to withstand the rape and the grief associated with abandoning her younger parts. Repairing this relationship is an important aspect of the healing process, and it often *happens slowly over time, requires mutual trust, and needs to be handled with care.*

GRATITUDE AND REGRET

As we work with extreme or proactive protective parts, they will eventually begin to feel heard, known, and seen in a way that allows them to comfortably begin to establish a newfound relationship with the client's current-day Self. As this Self-to-part relationship develops, common feelings will arise, including gratitude and regret. This newly formed relationship allows the Self to share its gratitude for how hard the part was trying to help and for the gifts that came along with its job.

For example, a client named Joseph said: "I really appreciate my résumé part. He brought so many wonderful opportunities to my life and helped me achieve excellence in my career."

His part, in turn, was able to receive this gratitude and, after many years, finally felt truly appreciated. In response, Joseph said: "He is smiling when I say that to him. He loves the recognition."

Equally as important, and often more poignant, is when the Self also compassionately shares in the sorrow and regret with the part, with remarks like: "I really get why you're feeling so bad. Going too broadly at work in the service of achievement, and not being able to dive deeply into your true passions, kept you from feeling joy and creativity. I also know that you may have lost out on deeper connections in life because of always working so hard to achieve. I'm sad for you too."

It's powerful to share this space with your client when both the Self and the part can join together in gratitude and regret in a heartfelt, compassionate, and non-shaming way over the gifts and shortfalls of the protective part's job. When this degree of intimacy develops between them, it suggests that the time is right to safely move forward toward the underlying wound.

GETTING PERMISSION

Once the Self of today is in a relationship with the target part, and that part's job and fear have been identified, the one remaining goal is to gain the part's permission to access the wound. Protectors often grant permission once they are given an offer they believe they can't refuse. Remember, these parts have been doing this job for a long time, and their attempt at protection has been deemed marginally effective at best.

The first offer often presented to protective parts occurs when a part begins to see, feel, and trust the presence of Self-energy. This provides the part a new and different option, the possibility of lightening their load, not having to work so hard, and letting down their guard for once. The part begins to experience the strength, power, and capacity of the Self. In turn, the part allows itself the luxury of slowing down the intensity and frequency of its load. It knows that its job is still necessary, as the wound is still present inside. But for the first time, help has arrived, and there's the option of some relief.

This is an interim solution to its problem; the part becomes aware that only when the wound is fully healed can it truly be freed from its protective role. Yet the respite feels good to an exhausted and overworked part. *This offer allows for a decrease in the constancy of its job because the part has the support and competence of Self-energy.*

As is the case with explicit versus implicit direct access, I'm also a fan of what I like to call *explicit permission* compared to *implicit permission*. I prefer to hear parts explicitly say: "Yes, then I'll give you permission. I'm nervous but I'm going to do it." Often, when parts feel validated, they'll spontaneously soften or step back (i.e., grant implicit permission). With implicit permission, though, you'll often notice that parts will jump back in when they get scared or overwhelmed by feelings.

Therefore, it's important to invest time up front in getting parts to genuinely feel heard, seen, and appreciated by the client's Self, as well as by the therapist, and for these parts to feel comfortable in giving explicit permission to proceed. When they grant full permission, protective parts rarely jump in as the unburdening process unfolds. There is also little, if any, backlash after healing happens, and the overall process usually takes much less time.

The Invitations

Once parts trust, settle into, and benefit from the offer of the Self's presence, it's time to provide them with one of three invitations:

1. *Deal with the overwhelm.* For example, offer the following: "What if we were able to guarantee that the little girl (an exile) or the suicidal part (an extreme protector) would promise not to overwhelm the system with their intense feelings? Would you be interested in that?"

2. *Offer a new role.* For example, suggest the following: "What if you no longer had to be anxious or depressed or eat in excess? Would you be interested in that? What would you rather do instead?"

3. *Offer to heal the wound.* For instance, recommend the following: "What if we were able to heal little Billy and you no longer needed to protect him? Might you be interested in that?"

These three invitations are quite compelling to protective parts. They offer the possibility that the part can be relieved of its duties. Dick Schwartz has said that an invitation "offers hope to a hopeless system."

Dealing with Overwhelm

As previously mentioned, addressing protector fears can be one of the more challenging therapist tasks and the cause of frustration and a loss of faith in the IFS model. With most trauma, and for complex PTSD in particular, coping with overwhelm is the most common protector fear to be addressed.

I've often heard Dick Schwartz say: "Once a part agrees not to overwhelm the system, it won't. It never goes back on its word." However, for a long time, this wasn't the case for me in my practice. I would ask client parts to not overwhelm, and they would agree but would consequently "storm the gate" by completely taking over my client when things started getting intense. I would ask myself: "What was I doing wrong?"

Over time, I've learned a few things about addressing overwhelm. First, you need to fully believe that parts are capable of not overwhelming the system and to embody this from a place of Self-energy before you can suggest it to the client's part with confidence. Now I say to parts: "I know you can do this. I'm sure of it. I don't think we should proceed unless you promise not to overwhelm Anthony. From my experience, nothing therapeutic happens when you relive your traumatic experiences. I want you and everyone else in there to be safe."

When parts continue to demonstrate apprehension, I'll say: "Would you like to practice this with me? I want you to share all that you're holding for Anthony. But I'm asking you to share it a little at a time or in manageable chunks. This way, Anthony will be able to stay present and be there for you in a way you haven't experienced before." Here, I'm using direct access with the client's overwhelmed part. I may even suggest that we perform a little experiment together and have the part share 1 or 2 percent of its feelings so that the part can directly experience its capacity not to overwhelm.

Now, I can say with confidence and experience that once a part promises not to overwhelm, it won't.

A New Job and Healing the Wound

Dick often says: "There are three things I continually offer a protective part. First, I give it control by saying, 'You're the boss. We aren't going to do anything without your permission.' Second, I validate its experience with words like 'I get why you are feeling this way' or 'That makes sense.' And third, I offer the protective part hope by saying, 'What if we were able to heal the wound?'"

Remember that protective parts had to do their job because it was the solution they devised when they were all alone and trying to manage overwhelming life experiences. They try to solve problems rooted in relational boundary crossings, power imbalances, shame, and humiliation. Protective parts pull from what they know and have internalized from their environment, and they are often young—with limited developmental and cognitive abilities.

Our job is to give protective parts back the control that was taken away from them, to validate their valiant efforts, and to then offer them an alternative solution to their problems. Sometimes I feel more like a salesperson than a therapist in this endeavor. Most of the time that I spend with protective parts involves selling them on the idea that, if they give us (the client's Self and me) space and permission, we can help them release the wounds they're so steadfastly protecting while simultaneously offering them a new role in the system. You may have to present this offer several times, sometimes even hundreds of times, to zealous protective parts before they establish enough trust in you and your client and are willing to step back. Clearly the solution they originally settled on isn't working so well or the client wouldn't be seeking therapy. But we don't need to point out the ineffectiveness of the protective part's job—it's already aware of this on some level. Instead, we can offer it a novel solution to its dilemma, one that the part hasn't thought of yet. We can invite it to unload the burden of its job and enjoy the freedom to move forward.

The following therapist-client dialogue underscores how this offer can work:

"What would I rather do? I've never even thought about that before. This has always been my role. This is all I've ever known," the client says.

"I'd like you to take a moment and just think about the possibility of being able to do something differently."

The client asks: "What would I do then?"

"Whatever you want to do. It's totally up to you. It's your choice."

"I'm going to need to sleep on that for a while. No one has ever offered me anything like that before."

"I'm offering this right now, and it's a real possibility for you."

The idea of being freed up to do something completely different is extremely enticing to protective parts. Their experience is that they *have* to do their job. They are like hamsters racing endlessly on a wheel, stuck in this repetitive role. And they're correct: They *do* have to continue performing this job until the wound heals. This is why I never spend too much time trying to convince parts to, for example, stop drinking or binging or obsessing. They feel like it's their duty. I respect their view but offer them a different option. Fortunately, they want help; they just haven't been able to find an alternative solution by themselves. The therapist's role is to provide hope.

Being respectful and getting permission are my main priorities when encountering traumatized protective parts. My job is to help them feel valued and appreciated for their heroic efforts, aid them in relinquishing their duties, and get them to allow us to unload the damage caused by other people's harsh words, poor behavior, and lack of caring.

WORKING WITH
PROTECTIVE PARTS IN TRAUMA

For best results, follow these steps:

1. Identify the client's target part.

2. Get the client to focus their attention internally.

3. Begin to explore the part with the client, and ask the part for some space (separation or unblending).

4. If the part is not willing to unblend, talk directly to the part (via direct access).

5. Once separation has occurred, identify Self-energy.

6. Foster the Self-to-part relationship.

7. If the part isn't interested in connecting with the Self, update the part to the current-day Self and have the Self apologize for its lack of support during the trauma.

8. Help the Self learn about the part's positive intentions, including its job and fears.

9. Address the part's fears, and help the part guarantee not to overwhelm the system.

10. Offer the part a new role, and get permission to heal its wounds.

The Neuroscience of Trauma and Dissociation

CHAPTER 10

The Neurobiology of PTSD

THE NORMAL FEAR RESPONSE

Fear is a normal response to alarming and out-of-the-ordinary situations. When we encounter something threatening, we respond on two different levels: (1) first unconsciously, through neurocircuits in the amygdala, which give rise to an automatic response, and then (2) consciously, through cognitive systems, such as the PFC and hippocampus, which give awareness to the emotion of fear (LeDoux, 2015). In other words, *we first respond unconsciously to a threat, and then we feel it consciously as fear.*

Fear is then *extinguished* when the ventromedial portion of the PFC regulates or calms down amygdala firing, and the hippocampus provides a context in which both learning and extinction can occur (LeDoux, 2015). For instance, your brain may tell your body: "That was scary, but we've experienced something like that before, we're safe, and we can handle this." We perceive a threat, we react, we're afraid, we process the fear, and then we recover. This can happen occasionally or several times a day, depending on the level of stress we encounter. Remember one of the central tenets of IFS: *All protective parts are organized around fear.* Asking a client, for example, "What are you *afraid* would happen if you didn't drink alcohol, get anxious, or withdraw?" is a way to get to the heart of this fear.

IMPLICIT AND EXPLICIT MEMORY

As we explore the neurobiology of PTSD and dissociation, it's important to look at how memories, as well as fear, are encoded and processed. There are two common ways that memory can get encoded: via implicit memory or explicit memory. *Implicit memory* typically gets encoded within the first 18 months of life. However, we can also encode implicit memory whenever something traumatic happens to us throughout our life. Implicit memories are not language-based but, rather, are stored as perceptions, emotions, and bodily sensations. Implicit memory primes us for future action, is unconscious, and lacks awareness that it comes from the past (Anderson, 2013). I believe that most exiles and some extreme reactive parts are rooted in implicit memory.

Explicit memory, on the other hand, begins to develop at two years of age, typically when we begin talking. It requires focused attention; is linear, factual, and conscious; and involves a sense of time and narrative (Anderson, 2013). The hippocampus is necessary for explicit memory to develop. In IFS, we enable our clients to become aware of the unconscious exiled parts of themselves, housed in implicit memory, and guide them through a process of witnessing, unloading, and coping with their painful pasts. In other words, we help them convert implicit memory to explicit memory, which I believe is the overarching goal of trauma therapy in general.

POST-TRAUMATIC STRESS DISORDER

We'll now explore what happens in the brain and the body when the threat is more extreme or involves repeated violations of a verbal, physical, or sexual nature that result in the development of PTSD.

There are three main areas of the nervous system that, when affected by trauma, result in neural network dysregulation and symptom production: (1) neuroendocrine (i.e., hormonal), (2) neurochemical (i.e., neurotransmitters), (3) and neuroanatomical (i.e., brain structures). It's constructive to examine each system to better understand how PTSD develops, keeping in mind that protective parts and wounds likely live in the mind and utilize or access these trauma-based networks to express themselves.

HORMONAL FACTORS

When a stressful event occurs, our body receives this information and transmits it via nerve cells to the thalamus. When the information is deemed emotionally relevant, it heads toward the amygdala, which unconsciously processes this information, resulting in a variety of different reactions. One such response involves the activation of the hypothalamic-pituitary-adrenal (HPA) axis, which secretes a series of hormones. First, the hypothalamus secretes something called corticotropin-releasing hormone (CRH), which, in turn, stimulates the release of adrenocorticotropic-releasing hormone (ACTH) from the pituitary gland, which ultimately stimulates the release of glucocorticoids—more commonly known as *cortisol* (the main stress hormone in the body, released from the adrenal glands located on the top of each kidney).

Hormones Released by the HPA Axis

Cortisol is what helps us mobilize and mount a response when something dangerous happens to us. It can be incredibly useful, even lifesaving under certain circumstances, but in excess it can be quite destructive. In moments of crisis, cortisol increases emotional stability and mobilizes glucose or energy for the fight-or-flight response. It's also a potent anti-inflammatory and anti-allergy agent. However, it can be quite harmful to the body when we are under stress for extended periods and a surplus builds up. It's known to be toxic to the hippocampus, it can cause protein breakdown and muscle wasting, and it's a potent immunosuppressant, which can increase the risk of infections, medical illnesses, and certain forms of cancer. Therefore, while the right amount of cortisol can be helpful, it can be harmful or neurotoxic in excess.

Under normal conditions, the release of cortisol activates the sympathetic nervous system and generates a negative feedback loop that quiets down both the hypothalamus and the anterior pituitary gland. However, it has been shown that this feedback mechanism is defective in certain individuals (due to increased negative feedback sensitivity of the HPA axis), which ultimately results in decreased levels of cortisol. Research also suggests that having low levels of cortisol at the time of a traumatic event can be a risk factor for the development of PTSD (Sherin & Nemeroff, 2011). Therefore, cortisol is now being studied as a potential treatment for acute trauma to help patients consolidate and process traumatic memories in the service of preventing the development of PTSD.

CHEMICAL FACTORS

Just as the amygdala stimulates the release of hormones as a result of a threat, it also releases several chemicals or neurotransmitters. We'll briefly review them now and learn how certain psychiatric medications that correct neurotransmitter imbalances can be helpful to treat the abnormalities created by trauma.

First, consider serotonin, or 5HT as it's commonly referred to. It's produced in a part of the brain called the dorsal and median raphe. Individuals with PTSD are known to have reduced serotonin, and these diminished levels are associated with hypervigilance, increased aggression, impulsivity, and enhanced formation of intrusive memories (Rege & Graham, 2017). Serotonin also regulates norepinephrine and CRH, both of which are excitatory and increase due to stress.

It's widely known that selective serotonin reuptake inhibitors (SSRIs) are the treatment of choice for PTSD. Restoring serotonin levels to normal amounts is shown to have an overall calming effect on the nervous system, as well as the body. SSRIs have also demonstrated an ability to restore PFC activity.

Next, we'll examine norepinephrine, one of the principal chemicals involved in the stress response. In the brain, norepinephrine primarily comes from an area called the locus coeruleus. When norepinephrine gets released, it becomes widely distributed to various parts of the brain involved in PTSD, including the PFC, amygdala, hippocampus, hypothalamus, periaqueductal gray (a structure affiliated with the freeze response), and thalamus. Norepinephrine increases fear, encodes emotional memory, and enhances arousal and vigilance (Sherin & Nemeroff, 2011). When the sympathetic nervous system is activated during stress, the adrenal glands release norepinephrine, in addition to cortisol, throughout the body (LeDoux, 2015), which contributes to symptoms such as increased heart rate, tingling sensations in the limbs, sweating, and increased breathing.

Medications that decrease norepinephrine levels in the body, such as propranolol (a beta blocker), or in the brain, like clonidine (an alpha-2 agonist), are extremely useful for decreasing excitability and treating acute trauma.

Dopamine is another excitatory neurotransmitter, like norepinephrine, which contributes to the development of anxiety, as well as fear conditioning. There's some evidence supporting a genetic component to the way dopamine is metabolized in the body that can determine whether or not someone will develop PTSD (Rege & Graham, 2017).

Atypical neuroleptics—such as quetiapine, risperidone, or aripiprazole, to name a few—are helpful in low doses for the treatment of dissociation. They partially block dopamine and the N-methyl D-aspartate (NMDA) receptor, which is connected to learning and memory.

Glutamate is the primary *excitatory* neurotransmitter in the brain, and stress directly triggers its release. Glutamate activates the NMDA receptor and is thought to contribute to the consolidation of traumatic memory and play a central role in the development of dissociation. It is toxic in excess and likely contributes to the loss of nerve cells in the hippocampus and PFC of PTSD patients (Sherin & Nemeroff, 2011).

Mood stabilizers, which decrease glutamate, can be an excellent treatment for PTSD. However, many of them have numerous side effects, which make them difficult to tolerate.

GABA, on the other hand, is the primary *inhibitory* or calming neurotransmitter in the brain. It is closely connected to the benzodiazepine receptor, which drugs like lorazepam or clonazepam act upon. Stress is known to alter the GABA-benzodiazepine receptor complex (Sherin & Nemeroff, 2011), which is probably why so many people with PTSD seek out benzodiazepines to calm an activated brain.

Benzodiazepines are effective in treating the anxiety and activation associated with PTSD. Unfortunately, they can interfere with memory consolidation and are addictive, so they should be used sparingly or only on an as-needed basis. Certain mood stabilizers also increase GABA levels and are, therefore, calming to the nervous system.

The following chart summarizes the chemicals associated with the development of PTSD, along with medications that can help provide some relief.

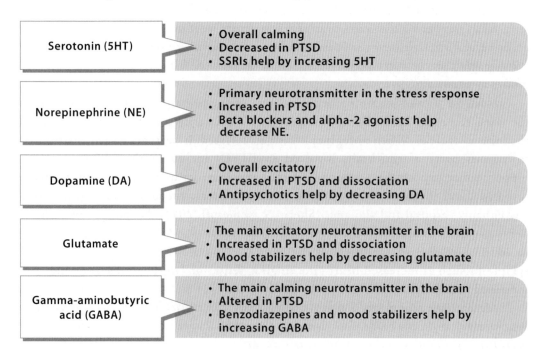

Serotonin (5HT)	• Overall calming • Decreased in PTSD • SSRIs help by increasing 5HT
Norepinephrine (NE)	• Primary neurotransmitter in the stress response • Increased in PTSD • Beta blockers and alpha-2 agonists help decrease NE.
Dopamine (DA)	• Overall excitatory • Increased in PTSD and dissociation • Antipsychotics help by decreasing DA
Glutamate	• The main excitatory neurotransmitter in the brain • Increased in PTSD and dissociation • Mood stabilizers help by decreasing glutamate
Gamma-aminobutyric acid (GABA)	• The main calming neurotransmitter in the brain • Altered in PTSD • Benzodiazepines and mood stabilizers help by increasing GABA

ANATOMICAL FACTORS

Neuroimaging studies have confirmed some of the key structural changes in the brains of PTSD patients. Among these are the hippocampus, amygdala, and PFC. The PFC includes the anterior cingulate cortex, insula, and orbitofrontal cortex (Sherin & Nemeroff, 2011).

The *hippocampus*, which helps reduce amygdala firing, is an important structure connected to learning, memory, and the elimination of fear. Reduced hippocampal volume is known to be a hallmark feature of PTSD. Cortisol and glutamate, both of which are excitatory, have been shown to impair new nerve growth and damage nerve cells in the hippocampus (Rege & Graham, 2017). Some researchers have speculated whether smaller hippocampal volume is a predisposing factor (or precursor) of PTSD development or a result of the toxic effects of the trauma itself (Sherin & Nemeroff, 2011).

The *amygdala* is crucial in helping us process emotions and extinguish fear. With increased stress, the amygdala releases glutamate, which encodes traumatic memories via the NMDA receptor, as previously mentioned. Studies have shown amygdala hyperresponsiveness and increased reactivity in clients who suffer from PTSD (Sherin & Nemeroff, 2011).

The *ventromedial portion of the PFC* exhibits inhibitory control over the stress response and emotional reactivity by suppressing amygdala firing (Sherin & Nemeroff, 2011). Individuals with PTSD have smaller PFC and anterior cingulate cortex volumes as a result of the noxious effects of trauma, and this loss in volume is thought to be a result of trauma, not a potential preexisting condition, as some have postulated is the case with the hippocampus (Rege & Graham, 2017).

Hippocampus	Amygdala	Prefrontal Cortex
• Calms amygdala firing • Reduced volume in PTSD • Preexisting condition or a result of toxic stress?	• Increases glutamate and consolidates trauma memory • Increased excitability and reactivity as a result of PTSD	• Reduces fear by inhibiting the amygdala • Reduced volume of ventromedial prefrontal cortex and anterior cingulate cortex in PTSD

It's not surprising that stress can negatively affect parts of the brain that are essential for recovering from threat, fear, and violation. And when that recovery isn't possible, symptoms consistent with PTSD arise. Luckily, the medications discussed earlier are known to be helpful in reversing some of these changes.

Even more remarkable, however, is IFS's ability to help clients access trauma-affected parts that are in some way associated with the hormonal, chemical, and structural changes in the brain and body. When we help our clients access Self-energy, they can unburden their wounds; release the thoughts, feelings, and sensations affiliated with their relational violation; and seemingly untangle and rewire their brains back to their original, non-traumatized states. This connection between IFS, trauma, and the brain is continually fascinating to me—a connection I hope we will continue to better understand and clarify through future research.

PUTTING IT ALL TOGETHER

In summary, when we experience an intrusion, we try our best to counteract the assault and recover from the threat. Sensory input from the body enters the thalamus, where it then moves up to the PFC and amygdala. Remember: The amygdala is quick and unconscious, and the PFC is slower and conscious in its processing of the information (van der Kolk, 2014). The amygdala responds by stimulating the release of hormones (CRH, ACTH, and cortisol) and chemicals (serotonin, acetylcholine, norepinephrine, and dopamine), activating the freeze response and regulating the sympathetic and parasympathetic nervous systems in an attempt to recover. The PFC and hippocampus then process the information and attempt to downregulate or calm down the activation in the amygdala (i.e., recovery or elimination).

When conditions are repeated, extreme, and void of love and connection, the amygdala releases glutamate (excitatory), which stimulates the release of large amounts of norepinephrine in the brain and body. Cortisol also continues to escalate until it eventually becomes depleted. These excitatory chemicals and hormones become toxic to the PFC and hippocampus, rendering them ineffectual in quieting the overwhelm, giving rise to the development of PTSD.

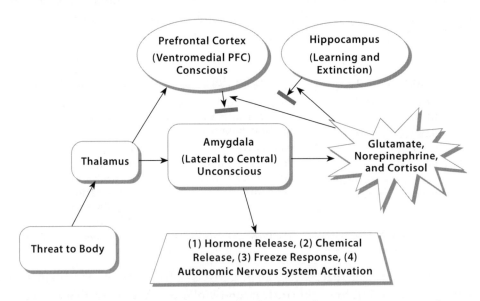

This excitatory response, shown in the diagram above, represents an "activated subtype" of PTSD described by Lanius and colleagues. Individuals with the activated subtype account for 70 percent of PTSD clients, and they exhibit reexperiencing and physiologic hyperarousal (Frewen & Lanius, 2015; Lanius et al., 2010). Neuroimaging studies have confirmed that these individuals exhibit low activation of the PFC and anterior cingulate cortex, which Lanius has called "failed inhibition" or the inability of the PFC to calm down or inhibit the amygdala from firing (Lanius et al., 2010). Here, emotions are high, the body is activated, and cognitions are low.

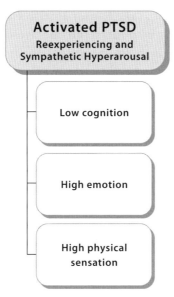

Now that we have discussed activated PTSD, take a moment to consider the other side of the story: when PTSD clients present with symptoms or parts that are blunted, numb, withdrawn, or dissociative. This type of blunted or dissociated PTSD accounts for 30 percent of clients (Frewen & Lanius, 2015), but it has been less thoroughly researched and is less understood compared to activated PTSD.

However, LeDoux and colleagues have been able to identify a shift within the amygdala that occurs with the avoidance response. Unlike the fear conditioning response, in which information travels from the lateral amygdala to the central amygdala, during the avoidance response, information goes from the lateral amygdala to the basal amygdala. *This redirected information inhibits the freeze response and activates a withdrawal reaction.* The basal amygdala connects with a structure in the brain called the ventral striatum (specifically the nucleus accumbens), which results in motor actions consistent with escape and avoidance (LeDoux, 2015). Here is a diagram showing the avoidance response.

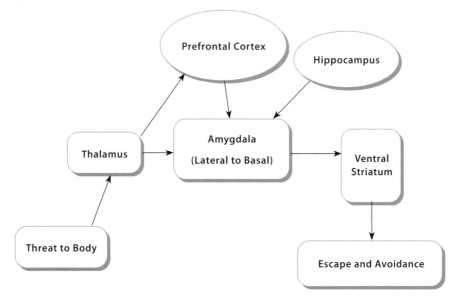

Stephen Porges, a scientist at the Kinsey Institute and professor at the University of North Carolina, also helps us understand the avoidance, dissociation, numbing, and shutdown responses through his polyvagal theory. His theory focuses on the autonomic nervous system and the different ways we react and respond to safety, stress, and life threat.

Porges describes how our body constantly and unconsciously assesses our surrounding environment to determine whether or not we're safe through a process he calls *neuroception* (Porges, 2017). When we experience safety in connection, the polyvagal theory maintains that the *ventral vagal branch of the parasympathetic nervous system* is active. However, when we experience danger, our *sympathetic nervous system* activates, causing us to respond in the familiar fight-or-flight manner. If we perceive that this danger is a life threat from which there is no escape, the *dorsal vagal branch of the parasympathetic nervous system* then activates, and we consequently disconnect, shut down, and dissociate as a survival mechanism (Porges, 2017).

Lanius has also described what happens in the brain for chronic PTSD survivors who exhibit avoidance, numbing, and dissociative symptoms. Neuroimaging studies show that individuals with this type of blunted PTSD exhibit the exact opposite response of those with hyperarousal, who show decreased PFC activity. In contrast, those with blunted PTSD exhibit an *increased* reaction in the PFC and anterior cingulate cortex. Lanius calls this state "overmodulation" or over-inhibition of emotional responsiveness (Lanius et al., 2010). With blunted PTSD, cognitive suppression is high while emotionality and physical sensations are low.

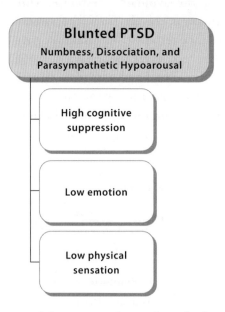

In summary, Lanius and her group have described two different subtypes of PTSD: a reexperiencing and hyperaroused type (activated PTSD) and a dissociative and hypoaroused type (blunted PTSD; Frewen & Lanius, 2015). In IFS, we think of these subtypes as different extreme protective parts that can express themselves in an activated or hyperaroused state, while other parts can protect in a blunted, withdrawn, or dissociative manner.

CHAPTER 11

Dealing with Extreme Parts: How Neuroscience Informs Therapeutic Decisions

It's helpful to further investigate these two different subtypes of PTSD and extreme parts—hyperaroused and hypoaroused—that attempt to protect traumatic wounds.

The intense reactions from parts commonly associated with relational trauma are typically what makes working with these clients so challenging. The severity and zealous nature of these first responder-type parts can challenge the best and most skilled therapist. It's important to remember, especially when the reactivity and intensity are unwavering, *that a protective part might need to unload or unburden itself before it's willing to permit access to the wound.* Extreme parts often hold so much anguish and self-loathing that they may opt to first release their pain before healing the wound.

When we're in the presence of extremely protective parts, we often don't have the luxury of being able to stop, to take a break, and to identify what's getting activated within ourselves before responding to them. As therapists, we need to do our best in the moment not to overreact—to hold the space for our client's activated parts and to assist them in feeling heard, seen, and validated for the ways they are trying to help. These parts often sabotage treatment, block progress, and detract from accessing internal pain and vulnerability. Neuroscience knowledge can aid therapists in making strategic therapeutic decisions that overcome these common roadblocks and help extreme parts more effectively unblend and give access.

When I think about extreme parts, I first like to focus on the *energy* they possess and present in the treatment room. For example, an alcohol-drinking part may say: "I'm so done with him. Give me the damn vodka now. I'm so pissed off that I could just kill him." The energy here is reactive and sympathetically hyperaroused. Compare that to another alcohol-drinking part presenting with energy in the resigned realm, which may say: "I'm done. What's the point? I give up. Give me the vodka—I'm out of here." Here the energy is more withdrawn, hopeless, and parasympathetically hypoaroused. The point is that parts can present with high or low energy, and it's important to differentiate between the two because each requires a different neuroscience-informed IFS response from the therapist.

Once you've determined the energy of your client's part, it's necessary to notice your own parts that may be present. Ask yourself: "How do I respond internally to the energy of my client's part?" Perhaps you find yourself thinking something like: "I'm sick of her coming in week after week complaining about that person and resorting to drinking as her only coping mechanism." This is an angry and activated response from one of your parts. Or you might be thinking: "My mind keeps wandering. This session feels like it's going on forever. Will this client ever get better?" This is a bored, distracted, and defeatist response from one of your parts.

It's important to identify our activated parts and ask them to give us space so we can be fully present for our clients' parts. The therapist's Self would respond with compassion, openness, and curiosity.

ACTIVATED AND HYPERAROUSED PARTS

When clients are blended with hyperaroused or high-energy parts, remember that neuroscience tells us they have little or no access to their PFC in these moments. This results in high emotion and high physical sensation, with little or no capacity for objectivity and reasoning. *Here, it's best to respond to them with compassion, not empathy.* Remember that compassion is caring about the other person's suffering with the desire to help. It has distance and perspective, is "unblended" in IFS terms, and is consistent with Self-energy. When your client's brain is temporarily unavailable to them, you can offer the separation, care, and perspective they need and are unable to provide for themselves.

You bring compassion to the part when you say things like: "You seem angry right now. But I know you'll be able to get through this. I'm here and available to help you in any way I can." This type of response is more likely to help the part relax and unblend.

If, on the other hand, you are more empathically resonate (i.e., feeling distress similar to your client), you run the risk of fueling the client's activation. This can happen when you offer a remark such as: "You look anxious right now. I know what that feels like. I feel a bit anxious right now too." Don't forget that emotions beget emotions.

When you're with a client with activated parts, try your best to maintain a caring, compassionate, and unblended stance. If this doesn't help them separate and their parts remain blended, I recommend moving to *direct access*. Lend them your PFC; in other words, have your Self engage in a dialogue with their aroused part, provided you have access to yours at that moment. Your Self can talk directly to their part, which is especially helpful when your client's brain is temporarily taken over and offline.

In summary, with activated, extreme parts, take the following steps:

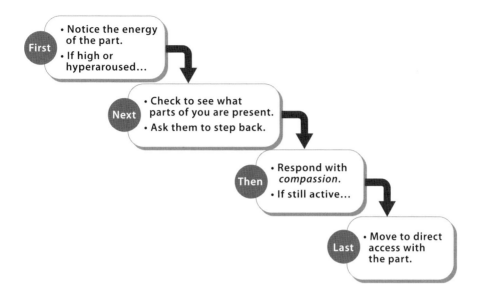

First
- Notice the energy of the part.
- If high or hyperaroused...

Next
- Check to see what parts of you are present.
- Ask them to step back.

Then
- Respond with *compassion*.
- If still active...

Last
- Move to direct access with the part.

NUMB AND DISSOCIATED PARTS

When the energy of the part is blunted, shamed, or withdrawn, clients can often internally experience this energy as being more problematic than hyperaroused energy. Porges reminds us that when we perceive a life threat, the dorsal branch of the vagus nerve activates. It's also well-known that it takes longer to recover from a state of shutdown than it does to recover from the fight-or-flight response. Additionally, we know that when we're withdrawn, the PFC is overactive (versus being underactive during arousal) and shuts everything down below it from the top down. This results in little or no access to thoughts, feelings, or physical sensations.

When you're with a client's part that presents with slow, low, or disconnected energy, I suggest that you first evaluate the degree to which their system is shut down at that moment. I might say something to the client like: "Can you wiggle your fingers right now? Are you feeling anything? What are you thinking about right now?" I assess how disconnected the client is from the bottom up—meaning body first, then feelings, followed by thoughts. Neuroscience teaches us that over-inhibition is a top-down process, so evaluating from the bottom up makes the most sense.

Once I've determined how disconnected the client is, I'll check in with myself to see if any of my parts are present. If not, I'll try to help the part unblend, this time with empathy instead of compassion. *Empathic resonance* is more likely to help the client bring their shutdown system back online. I would say: "I'm with you right now. I sense how upsetting that was for you. I know what it's like to be shamed. It really feels horrible. I can relate."

Again, if my empathic connection doesn't help the client's part unblend, I move into *direct access* using my Self-energy to connect directly with the client's shutdown part.

Try these steps:

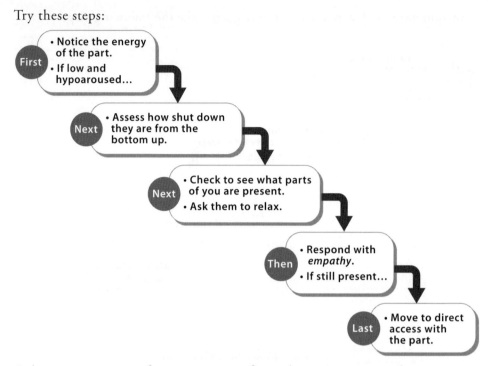

Below is a summary of neuroscience-informed interventions with extreme parts. It's important to note that with more severe trauma, such as DID, the parts that are present can rapidly alternate. It can be challenging to determine which part is present in a particular moment and what energy it's carrying. Having a clear game plan when encountering extreme traumatized parts is beneficial for therapists and clients alike. It enables clients' parts to relax and to unblend more quickly and minimizes the likelihood that therapists' parts will get activated.

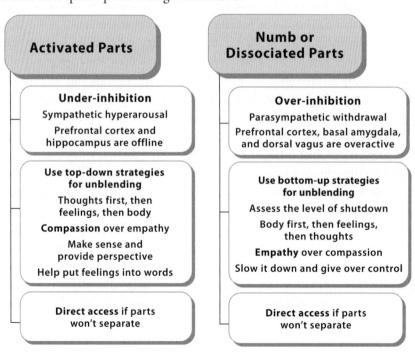

SECTION IV

Attachment and Relational Trauma

CHAPTER 12

The Stages and Styles of Attachment

HOW WE NORMALLY ATTACH

Gabor Maté and Gordon Neufeld state that attachment is at the heart of relationships and social functioning. They define attachment as the pursuit and preservation of proximity, closeness, and connection: physically, behaviorally, emotionally, and psychologically (Neufeld & Maté, 2014). Maté and Neufeld believe that there are six different ways children attach, which are through:

1. *Senses* (physical proximity)
2. *Sameness or identification* (being like the person you feel close to)
3. *Belonging and loyalty*
4. *Significance* (the feeling that we matter to someone)
5. *Feeling* (finding closeness through emotion, such as being warm, loving, affectionate, or emotionally intimate)
6. *Being known* (which they, like me, believe is the rarest of vulnerabilities and the hardest of all to do; Neufeld & Maté, 2014)

They also state that these ways of attaching underlie the drive for connection. This is at the heart of relational trauma: the natural desire to attach and connect, followed, unfortunately, by betrayal, abandonment, and violation.

Children do have a biological instinct to attach, which is a matter of survival (van der Kolk, 2014). Research on attachment suggests that the quality of parental care within the first two years of life promotes an "attachment style" for a child and sets a template for future relationships in adulthood (Fisher, 2017). Additionally, these early bonding experiences are later remembered not as visual or verbal narratives but as implicit memories and learned autonomic, motor, visceral, and behavioral responses. This sets the stage for affect tolerance, self-soothing, and an integrated sense of self later in life (Fisher, 2017).

It's generally believed that healthy parent-child interactions from a young age help children develop a secure attachment style that enables them to form stable and positive relationships in adulthood. However, when things go awry during this stage of development, it is also believed that lifelong relational difficulties can emerge.

ATTACHMENT STYLES

There are four main attachment styles that have been identified: secure, avoidant, anxious, and disorganized. Research shows that 62 percent of the general population is securely attached, 15 percent is avoidantly attached, 9 percent is anxiously or ambivalently attached, and 15 percent has what is called disorganized attachment (van der Kolk, 2014).

It is believed that children develop secure attachment when they grow up in an environment where their mother is responsive and attuned to their needs. *Securely attached* children develop an internal locus of control. They know what makes them feel good or bad, and they have developed a sense of agency (van der Kolk, 2014).

However, children who are raised by a mother who is unresponsive or rejecting become *insecurely attached*, causing them to respond in one of two different ways. (Consider, however, that all the prominent research published involves studies of mothers, which I have issues with for obvious reasons. After all, what about the role of fathers, especially when they are the primary caregiver?) One reaction of the insecurely attached child is to become *anxious* or hyperaroused, often crying, yelling, complaining, and acting needy. The insecurely attached child can also become *avoidant* or hypoaroused. These children act aloof and uninterested, as if nothing matters or bothers them (van der Kolk, 2014).

Meanwhile, children develop *disorganized attachment* in response to mothers who appear to be hostile or intrusive and helpless or fearful (Lyons-Ruth & Block, 1996). These children appear frightened without having a clear solution for connection. Karlen Lyons-Ruth, a professor of psychology at Harvard University, has studied attachment and become particularly interested in this disorganized attachment group. She has found that a mother's emotional withdrawal, not her intrusiveness, has the most profound and long-lasting effect on her child's mental instability (Lyons-Ruth & Block, 1996). Lyons-Ruth has also found that children are much more likely to develop dissociative symptoms in young adulthood if they are raised by mothers who are disengaged and misattuned during the child's first two years of life. These young adults feel lost, overwhelmed, and disconnected and see themselves as unloved, empty, and helpless (Lyons-Ruth, 2003).

Attachment theory demonstrates the importance of healthy "good enough" parenting on a child's development and also alerts us to the mental health and relational difficulties that can ensue when a child is relationally neglected, ignored, and repeatedly intruded upon. This data is consistent with the ACE study results discussed in chapter 2.

A DIFFERENT VIEW OF ATTACHMENT DISORDERS

I agree with the necessity and importance of good quality connection for the safety and well-being of children. Children cannot survive without being attached. Connection is one of the most important things in life—for both children and adults.

However, I have a different view of attachment styles as they relate to IFS therapy. I don't necessarily believe in attachment styles per se, nor do I believe that they get firmly established within the first two years of life. *I do believe that different parts of children attach to different parts of caregivers throughout their life.* For example, a part of me developed an anxious attachment to the part of my mother that often denied reality. Another part of me developed an avoidant connection to the part of my mother that could be intrusive at times.

I also believe that parts of me securely attached to the parts of her that were eternally loving and supportive (i.e., her Self). I have parts that developed a disorganized relationship to her confusing and often contradictory parts too. I don't think these are permanent or entrenched styles of me, and I don't believe this is the way I relate to most of the people in my adult life. *I contend that most attachment styles, when seen through an IFS lens, are wounds or protective parts that develop as a result of difficult or challenging interactions* and that they have a big influence on our lives as adults, especially when they're not adequately addressed or healed. I contend that we each have different parts that relate to different parts of other people. I further posit that we have experiences with each of these "styles" or "different parts," which connect to the various parts of people with whom we're in connection.

I have experienced this same phenomenon from the opposite side—as a parent with my children. They know whom to ask when they want someone to cook for them, whom to approach when they want to go biking or play on the trampoline, and whom to avoid when they fight with each other. I believe that both of my boys feel safe and secure when they are in connection with me when I'm in Self-energy. I also observe that they've had confusing and disorganizing experiences when I lose my temper and become someone totally different to them in those moments. At first, they connect with the reasonable, calm, non-triggered part of their father; it undoubtedly shocks them when an extreme, irrational, and intense part of me takes over. One minute I'm the reasonable father they know and love, and the next moment I'm triggered and present in a completely different way. This must be confusing for them, especially if I don't take responsibility for my actions and fail to apologize after I've recovered. Unfortunately, this is the case for many complex trauma survivors: The parent doesn't own their piece, and the child internalizes it, assumes responsibility, and tries to make sense of it on their own.

I often encounter clients who would certainly fit a disorganized attachment style. But when you approach them using an IFS lens, you quickly see that there are two different parts with two different views that have developed as a result of complicated relational dynamics. These clients often have parts that think: "Relationships are dangerous; I must stop them at all costs" (a protector) and "I'm desperate for connection; I'll do whatever it takes to keep that person in my life" (a wound). I feel that disorganized attachment can be more disorganizing for the person who is in relationship with these two different parts, not for the person who holds the opposing views. But when we see this from an IFS perspective, we take a curious stance and listen to both parts; they both make perfect sense. It becomes clear, not disorganized.

Here is how attachment theory can be viewed through an IFS lens:

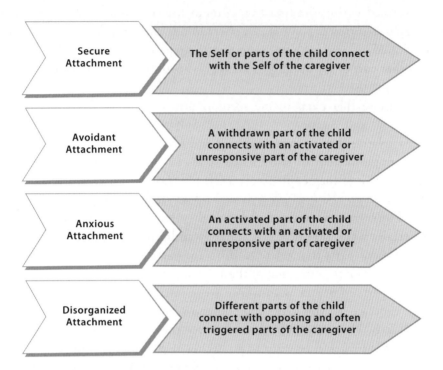

Secure Attachment	The Self or parts of the child connect with the Self of the caregiver
Avoidant Attachment	A withdrawn part of the child connects with an activated or unresponsive part of the caregiver
Anxious Attachment	An activated part of the child connects with an activated or unresponsive part of caregiver
Disorganized Attachment	Different parts of the child connect with opposing and often triggered parts of the caregiver

CHAPTER 13

IFS as Internal Attachment Work

THE POWER OF ATTACHMENT TRAUMA

The parts that develop as a result of ongoing young attachment wounding can be potent and subtly pervasive. They can dominate a person's life, especially when that person enters adulthood and attempts to engage in intimate relationships. I believe that most, if not all, attachment wounds live within implicit memory, which is persistent, largely unconscious, and has no time sequence or narrative associated with it.

I've encountered many clients who struggle with this issue. In thinking about this problematic prevalence, the song "Run the World (Girls)" by Beyoncé comes to mind, funnily enough. Only instead of the standard lyrics, "Who run the world? Girls," in my mind the lyrics change to "Who run the world? Exiles." Because exiles, the parts that carry wounds, are legion. Think about it: Young and desperate attachment wounds actually *do* run the world and make most of our relational decisions for us. *Attachment trauma couples the past with an attempt at redemption in the present.* IFS helps clients to "uncouple" the past from the present, making the pull to relive much less likely.

Adults typically have free will and choice when it comes to decisions about relationships. They can choose to stay, or they can choose to leave a painful, unsatisfying, or abusive relationship. Children are not afforded this same luxury; they are forced to stay. When adults suffer from a history of repeated relational betrayals when they are young, and they haven't done the work to heal those wounds, they tend to repeat them. Adults often remain tethered to their past, believing they can't leave, and reenact their childhood experiences with their adult partners.

These young attachment wounds make most of the relational decisions in adulthood, and they do so in the service of trying to fix the past. They may think, for instance: "This guy will treat me better than my father did" or "She'll love and accept me in a way that my mother never could." But these parts still hold past beliefs and internally respond with thoughts like: "I can't leave. Men have all the power—they're always in charge" or "Women are usually controlling. If I speak up, I'll most likely get criticized." These exiled parts are at the root of attraction and desire, but they're ill-equipped to maneuver adult relationships in a healthy, mature way. This sets the stage for repeated, abusive relational reenactments of young attachment wounds in adulthood.

Healing these wounds allows one to relationally choose from a different place, not from a place of the past or out of hope for repair and redemption but from a place of adult openheartedness and Self-energy. When working with clients who haven't dealt with their attachment trauma, we often feel the energy and power of these young parts. Yet they're often below the radar and rarely named. However, these young parts are ever-present and palpable and have a powerful influence over our clients' lives. And when we finally acknowledge and address them in therapy, these exiles can take months to years to heal.

DIFFERENT ATTACHMENT WOUNDS

In my experience, these attachment wounds often consist of a series of hurts and betrayals that occur over several years and are held in one main part. I call this central part the *collective attachment wound,* which is a series of traumas brought together under one main exile. This exile is often referred to as "my little one" or given a name like "Little Tony" or "Tiny Samantha."

Consider the plight of a client we'll call Daniel. Daniel was a high-achieving computer engineer, always at the top of his class. He constantly attempted to date the most attractive woman he could find to subsequently marry and have children with. After many failed attempts, Daniel finally found what he called the "perfect wife," with whom he raised a family. Daniel would frequently come into therapy sessions following a disagreement with his wife, saying: "I'm such a failure, I can't stop her from being mad at me. I wouldn't blame her if she decided to leave."

Nothing was ever good enough for Daniel, and he was never satisfied with how things turned out in his life. But after meeting many of his intense protective parts, Daniel was able to connect with a younger part of him who grew up feeling "less than" and inadequate. Daniel's life suddenly had a context that made sense to him.

"I'm blown away right now meeting this 'little guy,'" he told me. "I can't believe how every single choice in my life up to this point has been driven by him. He feels so insufficient and defective. Most, if not all, of my decisions have been a desperate attempt to try and counteract how this little guy feels about himself. This work we've done on my parts is incredible."

It's also possible in attachment trauma to have several different exiles hold similar painful experiences over many years. I refer to these as *developmental wounds*, which we will discuss further in chapter 23. Case in point: A 3-year-old part, a 9-year-old part, and a 16-year-old part all carry the experience of being physically abused by their mother. This type of wounding can also have a powerful impact on adult relational decision making.

Consider the case of Olivia, a pediatrician who came in to see me because she was unhappy in her second marriage. She had three children: two from a previous marriage and one with her current partner. She struggled with a harsh internal critic part that would also intermittently lash out at her husband, as well as an intellectual part that kept her away from most, if not all, of her feelings. But her clinical profile never really made sense to me. She didn't seem to have a history that was consistent with her symptoms and life struggles. I couldn't connect her intimacy difficulties with any comprehensible history.

Slowly, we were able to perform cumulative healing work that was consistent with what many therapists would call "small 't' trauma." We helped a part Olivia had that felt ignored as a child while away at camp. Another part that felt less important than and in the shadow of her older sister. A third part that was fiercely yelled at by her father, once when he was "overserved" at a wedding. And a different part that felt shamed in middle school by the popular girls who teased her for not being athletic. Much to our surprise, Olivia began to feel much stronger and more confident in her life. She was able to speak up at work and at home with her husband in fresh, positive, and constructive ways. She became a stronger parent and felt increasingly happier, now desiring to taper off her prescribed antidepressant.

"I had no idea that all those events in my childhood had such a huge impact on me," she said. "I realize that each of these experiences held some shame and the feeling of being less than. I think all the little pain added up over time and had a huge impact on me."

"I'm so happy that we were able to help all your parts release what they were holding onto," I replied.

It's important to keep in mind that not all of the energy and decisions motivated by attachment wounds are negative. These young parts can create stamina and an internal drive that can help clients achieve some incredible things in their lives. "I would never have gotten through medical school had it not been for those younger parts of me," Olivia said. "These parts have helped me so much throughout my life, now it's time for me to help them."

SEPARATION AND PREVERBAL TRAUMA

With attachment wounds in particular, separation—or helping parts unblended from the Self—can be challenging. These parts often present as if they are holding on for dear life, and the need to stay connected often feels to them like a matter of survival. The idea of softening or detaching from the Self, even slightly, seems utterly impossible.

Here's where therapist creativity comes in handy. I suggest finding imaginative ways to convince your client's young needy parts that separation is possible and helpful, despite this supposed paradox of separation. For example, I'll often engage in direct access with these young parts, saying something like: "If you're willing to separate from Dan just a little bit, he'll be able to be with you in the way you've always wished and you won't have to be alone any longer." I'll then make a suggestion that includes some form of separation accompanied by continued connection: "Maybe if you hold his hand or sit on his lap and try looking at Dan, you'll be able to feel more connected to him?" Your goal is to be imaginative and resourceful with suggestions that encourage separation yet still allow for contact, which these parts crave and desperately need to feel safe.

Attachment trauma can also show up in preverbal forms. Remember that within the first two years of life—when only implicit memory is present—abandonment, betrayal, and intrusive experiences are encoded without words. Parts are, however, still quite capable of communicating, even when language is not developed. They can express themselves through feelings, physical sensations, visual images, sound, and amazingly, transmission of thought. I encourage my clients to be open to all of the ways their parts want or need to communicate with them.

There tends to be an order of communication when it comes to preverbal parts. It typically follows *a bottom-up pattern of transmission*. For example: Physical sensations present themselves first, followed by the expression of emotion, and last, the story or narrative reveals itself. It's also common for preverbal parts to *start out inanimate or one-dimensional and to evolve into human form* as the Self gets to know them better.

Take the example of Fatima, a client of mine who would often say that her body felt the need to move as she sheepishly asked me if she could lay down on the couch in my office during sessions. She slowly began to move in an unorthodox rhythmic manner for several sessions in a row before she also began to cry. I had the sense that I just needed to stay present and to hold space for her as this process unfolded, not really knowing where it was heading. Eventually, the sensations and feelings were connected to a memory that she was ultimately able to put into words. She described a baby in the back seat of a car who witnessed her brother tragically die in a car crash. This preverbal memory, of which Fatima had no prior awareness, was eventually unburdened, and much to her surprise, her lifelong fear of driving also resolved.

We can even encounter parts who communicate in utero, as demonstrated by the following case example. Here, it's important to have any of your skeptical parts step back and to allow the process to unfold organically. These scenarios can also be difficult for clients to trust, but, over time, they usually make sense and fit together like pieces of a puzzle in the context of their life.

BEFORE WORDS—BRANDON (TO BRIANNA)

Brandon, a 24-year-old who is in the process of transitioning, recently encountered a roadblock in therapy:

> "For some reason, I'm really struggling with using she/her pronouns. I know I've always felt trapped in this male body, and my Self knows I'm a woman, but something is preventing me from taking this next step in my transition."

> "Well, let's check inside for a moment and see if we can learn more," I said.

> "I just hear, 'We're wrong, we're wrong, no one will ever love us.'"

> "Let those parts know that you're hearing them, Brandon, and that we're here to help them."

> "Now I'm now seeing the parts that tried so hard to fit in. I see myself looking at Uncle Mike, trying to act and move like he did so I would look normal. I see myself playing Star Wars with the boys next door, always secretly wanting to be Princess Leia but knowing to keep those thoughts to

myself. I even remember the look of disgust I got from people when one of my girl desires accidently leaked out. I was trying to be someone else my whole entire childhood. It's so sad."

"Yes, it is, Brandon. Try to send these parts some love and appreciation for the ways they tried to help you over the years."

"They really like that. They really saved my life, you know."

"Yes, I know they did," I responded.

"I'm now seeing a tiny infant in what appears to be a womb or something. It sensed that something was drastically wrong. I'm getting the sense that the baby felt defective and unworthy of love," Brandon said.

"Brandon, if it feels right in your heart, can you let the infant know you're getting all of this? Can you send it love and let it know it's perfect just the way it is?"

"It really loves hearing that and, for the first time ever, is able to take in love. It's relaxing and seems so calm right now. This is exactly what this baby needed. It's incredible, it's letting me know from its heart that we were a 'her' from the very beginning and that our name is Brianna, not Brandon."

"That's beautiful," I responded with a tear in my eye. "Let the infant know that we're going to do our best to help the outside better match the inside."

"She loves that!" Brianna said.

The Client's Self as Therapeutic Agent: Repairing the Internal Relationship

Attachment-centered therapies tend to focus on developing or rebuilding trusting relationships between the therapist and client, with the hopes of correcting and repairing the client's unhealthy attachment patterns that developed earlier in life. I believe that attachment and connection are more than merely important: They're vital in healing the chasm created by complex relational violations. However, as I've stated previously, IFS maintains that: (1) the relationship between a client's Self and their wounded part is primary, and (2) the therapeutic relationship between the therapist and client is secondary regarding healing wounds. No one can correct or repair the hurt caused by the past like the Self can—not even the best of therapists.

Attachment and the Corrective Experience

During a therapy session, a client of mine named Joan achieved an unburdening with a younger part of her that felt left out and ignored by her summer camp counselors when she was 11 years old. A week later, Joan arrived for her weekly session.

Here is the dialogue we engaged in:

"How is your younger part doing? Have you been checking in with that 11-year-old daily as you promised you would?" I asked.

"Things are going pretty well, I think. The girl is starting to feel a new level of confidence within herself," she said.

"That's great, Joan. But what do you mean by 'I think?'"

"While I was checking in with her over the week, she moved back into the past and I'm not sure why," Joan said.

"Is there more she wanted to share?" I asked.

Joan's 11-year-old part proceeded to tell Joan about her older sister Samantha—and how much the young Joan loved, looked up to, and missed her elder sibling.

"I wanted to be just like her. She was interesting, and I wasn't. Everyone liked Samantha," the young part replied.

"Let's ask your younger part more about that, Joan," I said.

After a few moments of silence, the woman before me quietly began to cry.

"It was all about my mother's love and attention," Joan said. "That little girl knew my mother loved her oldest daughter more. Samantha was smarter, prettier, and more well-liked by all the children at camp. The little girl thought that if she was more like Samantha, maybe her mom would like her too."

We both paused for a moment, reflecting on the feelings behind the statement. I asked, "Joan, what would you like to say to her about that?"

"I'm brokenhearted that you didn't get the attention you needed from Mom," Joan's Self told her 11-year-old part. "You are interesting. Your day was interesting. You are worth listening to. You are lovable. I love you."

"Is she listening to you and receiving what you're saying?" I asked.

"Yes, totally. I love that I can time travel and give her what she needed and wanted back then. She is so happy right now. We are walking together and holding hands."

"That's beautiful," I told her with a smile.

"What would you like to say to her about that?" is one of those very important questions we ask when Self-energy is present with an exiled part. *The Self is the ultimate corrective experience.* When the original person—in this case, Joan's mother—isn't able to offer love, comfort, and healing, the Self serves as the next best thing. Here, the Self is incredibly powerful and giving—and in speaking from the heart, it provides the part what it needs and wants.

Beware: Parts easily get attached to the therapist as the hoped-for corrective object. Nine times out of ten, the part will choose the therapist over the client's Self as its healing agent. Remember that the therapist didn't abandon the part. That's why it's important to be mindful of our therapist caretaking parts here. If we're not careful, we can foster this relationship in a way that reinforces the breach between the client's Self and the part. The more attached these parts get to us, the harder it becomes, as Dick Schwartz says, to *pass the baton* back to the client's Self as the primary healing agent, which is the goal.

RELATIONSHIPS, TREATMENT, AND ATTACHMENT TRAUMA

During treatment with survivors of attachment trauma, there's often a particular order or rhythm that occurs when it comes to their adult relationships. Initially, many survivors will be overly dependent on the people they're connected with. Their younger parts show up and can be experienced as desperate, needy, and overwhelming to those around them. When clients enter treatment and therapists begin the process of helping them begin to separate from their younger parts, a natural shift occurs in the needs and priorities of their external relationship. During this stage, clients tend to become more independent and self-reliant. They often end unhealthy, codependent relationships and spend time getting comfortable with themselves, sometimes preferring to live alone for a while.

I often get excited for my clients during this stage of beginning independence, which is important for them both internally and externally. I may think to myself: "Finally, Jim can stand on his own two feet, be on his own, and disengage from unhealthy serial relationships. Jim is getting comfortable with himself and his parts, and for the first time in his life, he doesn't need someone else in order to function and be happy. He is benefitting from the strength of self-independence."

As the therapist, it's important to observe this stage carefully and to ensure that the client doesn't get *too* comfortable and settle in for the long haul. Using the previous client as an example, consider that Jim could become happy on his own and start to avoid relationships and intimacy altogether, as his memories of them are painful, heartbreaking, and unsuccessful. Instead, I want to help Jim appreciate his newfound separateness but not let him get too entrenched in this comfort zone. I need to gently nudge Jim into gravitating toward past pain so that he can begin healing deeply buried relational wounds. Then I want to guide him toward a place of open curiosity and nurture a true desire for connection with someone from a place of Self-energy. I don't want him to remain in a place of isolation, avoidance, and fear of intimacy.

In summary, clients with attachment trauma often start out needy in relationships and can settle into an unhealthy zone of solo comfort. It's our job as therapists to assist them in addressing their pain, healing their wounds, and emerging with a fresh desire for intimacy that's genuinely driven by their Self, not by their redemption-influenced past parts.

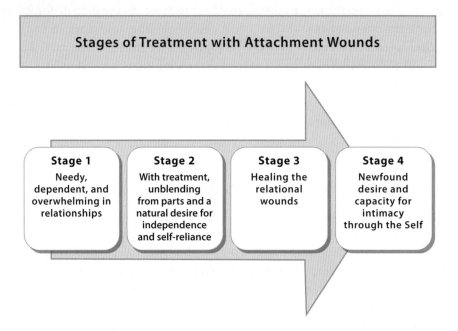

Stages of Treatment with Attachment Wounds

Stage 1
Needy, dependent, and overwhelming in relationships

Stage 2
With treatment, unblending from parts and a natural desire for independence and self-reliance

Stage 3
Healing the relational wounds

Stage 4
Newfound desire and capacity for intimacy through the Self

NEUROSCIENCE: THE SCIENCE BEHIND CONNECTION

Lane Beckes and James Coan, researchers from the University of Virginia, have conducted research demonstrating the obvious: *connection is important and valuable*. However, what is unique about their work is that they have validated their findings from a neuroscience perspective. Social baseline theory (SBT), as they call it, holds that the presence of other people helps us conserve important and often metabolically costly somatic (bodily) and neurological resources through the social regulation of our emotions (Beckes & Coan, 2011). In other words, relationships help us manage our emotions without needing to utilize our own physical or neurological resources.

Beckes and Coan have determined that the quality of our connections helps us regulate or recover from negative emotions in the brain. The neural structures we typically recruit to manage our emotions are *less* active when high-quality social support is available. When we maintain social connection, our brains are less vigilant in response to threats, and we do not need to engage in emotional self-regulation. Put another way, closeness represents an innate *baseline* strategy for human emotion regulation, one that doesn't require deliberate action on our behalf (Beckes & Coan, 2011).

These researchers have also studied how women respond when confronted with a shock or threat across three different scenarios: while they were alone, holding a stranger's hand, or holding a partner's hand. Women with the highest-quality relationships (i.e., holding a partner's hand) required the least brain activity to recover. The physical connection with their partners allowed them to recuperate more quickly while expending less brain energy. As the quality of this connection lessened, they needed to recruit more brain structures to recover. All three groups of women recruited the right anterior insula, superior frontal gyrus, and hypothalamus.

However, women who held a stranger's hand *additionally* recruited the superior colliculus, right dorsolateral PFC, caudate, and nucleus accumbens. Women who were alone also engaged the ventral anterior cingulate cortex, posterior cingulate, supramarginal gyrus, and postcentral gyrus to recover from the threat.

The point here is not to memorize all of the brain structures involved in rebounding from a threat. Instead, it's useful to appreciate the importance of connection as it relates to recovering from stress and trauma. *Self-regulation*, or recovering from a threat while alone, requires our brain and body to work hard, utilizing excess energy and internal resources to help inhibit or downregulate the emotional activation caused by a peril. With a safe, high-quality connection present, the women didn't need to expend energy to bounce back from the threat; they didn't even mount an emotional response.

Having a connection was shown to decrease cardiovascular arousal, facilitate the development of a non-anxious temperament, inhibit the release of stress hormones, reduce threat-related neural activation, and generally promote health and longevity. Conversely, social subordination, rejection, and isolation were shown to be powerful sources of stress and compromised health (Beckes & Coan, 2011).

In summary, attachment and connection are important to all of us at any age. When we're engaged in healthy, higher-quality relationships, our parts are less often activated, the Self is more present, and it's easier and less taxing to overcome a violation. When we're alone or in unsatisfying relationships, we can still recover but our protective parts get triggered more easily, we expend more emotional energy, and we stress our nervous system in response to a perceived danger.

Under more severe circumstances or with repeated relational trauma, it becomes much harder, if not impossible, for us to recuperate. Extreme parts, ranging from hyperaroused to dissociative, become activated and attempt to fend off the pain and anguish caused by the assault. When recovery isn't possible, PTSD develops, symptoms persist, and parts get stuck in time, either trying their best to keep overwhelming feelings locked away or constantly reliving these emotions each time they get triggered.

Fortunately, IFS offers hope and a way to reverse and release the chronicity of the relationally traumatic experiences for all those who have been afflicted.

SECTION V

Common Reactions to Relational Trauma

CHAPTER 14

Vulnerability

Vulnerability: A Four-Letter Word

At the core of most, if not all, relational wounding is a violation of our vulnerable selves—our young parts that represent the jewels of our personality. The vast array of protective responses that develop as a result of this breach are primarily designed to ward off the pain carried by our exiled parts. People often equate being vulnerable with being hurt and, therefore, try to avoid being vulnerable at all costs. I feel this is a *distorted belief* that developed as a result of trauma and that we, as therapists, can help our clients revisit this view from another perspective, one that corrects the distortion and includes the Self.

My clients frequently react to my suggestion that they should try being vulnerable with their partner, friends, or children as if I were speaking to them in a foreign language. They appear to have an allergic reaction to the idea, uttering incredulous responses such as: "Are you kidding me?" "Why would I do that?" "It's just a sign of weakness," and "That's the reason I got hurt in the first place—don't you get that?"

The definition of *vulnerability* in the Oxford English Dictionary is: "The quality or state of being exposed to the possibility of being attacked or harmed, either physically or emotionally." Logically, vulnerability would be experienced as something to be avoided when it's associated with being hurt or wounded instead of being associated with the expression of what we feel deep inside ourselves.

Brené Brown speaks to our cultural perception of vulnerability as predominantly a weakness and redefines it as a strength instead of a deficit. She says: "Vulnerability is the core of all emotions and feelings. To feel is to be vulnerable. Vulnerability is the birthplace of love, belonging, joy, courage, empathy, and creativity" (Brown, 2012, pp. 33–34). She further defines vulnerability as uncertainty, risk, and emotional exposure.

I agree that vulnerability is a superpower, not a weakness. *I see vulnerability as comprising two different components: (1) Self-connection, or the ability to connect with what we feel or to our truth; and (2) the ability to share it with another person.* To me, being vulnerable is being genuine or authentic with ourselves as well as with another. It means not wavering or leaving our truth and not worrying about the other person and their reaction or response to the expression of our true feelings.

A more common response from a trauma survivor might be: "If I'm honest and vulnerable, I'll lose this relationship. Do I disconnect from what I know to be true to save this relationship? Have I ever really known or been able to connect with what I feel?"

Being vulnerable can feel like a big risk, as Brené Brown describes, especially when you have repeatedly been slammed, shamed, criticized, or attacked for expressing yourself in the presence of another person (Brown, 2012). This, unfortunately, is all too common for complex trauma survivors, many of whom have found that connecting to and sharing what they feel with another person will only lead to something horrible; hence, they don't do it. Once you have been repeatedly hurt in this way, you develop an elaborate protective mechanism to keep the emotional pain away. *One of the great gifts of IFS therapy, as it relates to complex trauma, is its reversal of the suffering that resulted from our truth being attacked by another.*

To be seen and known, warts and all, and to be who you truly are—openly and freely in connection with another person—can certainly be scary. But it also can be exhilarating, amazing, and enormously freeing when it goes well. In its most basic form, to be vulnerable is to be intimate with our self and others.

I spent many hours in therapy before I could fully embrace this idea of loving who I am and feeling confident and comfortable to freely express this to the people in my life—especially as a gay man with a trauma history. Yet the rewards have been immeasurable, as evidenced by a higher happiness quotient. The older I get, the more "myself" I become and the more I'm able to express this truth to others with clarity and confidence. My journey is by no means over; instead, I will always be in therapy and continue to evolve, expand, and unfold in wonderful and surprising ways.

Reactions to Feelings

Many trauma survivors who still carry portions of their trauma inside themselves don't fully understand yet that it's their perpetrator's reaction to their feelings that's the real problem, not the expression of their vulnerability. Remember: Complex PTSD, as we've defined, is typically regarded as a violation of a relationship. I believe that the problem developed because of the way the other person responded, how they reacted, and what they said or did. "It's about their parts, not yours," I tell my clients. A burden is created because a part got hurt and was forced to hold the pain around *the response* to the expression of their truth. Once again, it's not the expression of our feelings that's the problem; *it's the reaction to them.* And this gets confused all the time, particularly with children, who typically will take responsibility for what was said and done to them, especially when the other person—usually an adult—doesn't.

It boils down to confusion around the issue of *responsibility*. Who's responsible for what? During therapy sessions, I sometimes hear clients' parts say, "I'm sick of you! How many times do I have to tell you to shut up already?" (much like a parent yelling at their child) or "I'm an idiot. It's my fault. I'm such a loser" (much like a child will respond to verbal abuse). These types of responses are often critical internalized perpetrator parts trying to take control of something that feels scary and painful. When kids are left alone with their traumatic experiences, they need to make sense of the situation, and they often take responsibility for what was done to them. *This is how distorted beliefs get embedded and how vulnerability gets blamed as the problem.*

VULNERABILITY AND CONNECTION

Gabor Maté talks about two basic needs that all human beings have: (1) the need for attachment, and (2) the need for authenticity (knowing what we feel and being able to express who we are; Maté 2011). He further describes what happens when the two are not aligned. When children receive information about themselves that doesn't align with their authentic Self, they have to choose between the two; they will often choose attachment over authenticity for the sake of survival (Maté 2011). They disconnect or suppress their true Self to survive. Maté believes that repeated misalignment or disconnection can later manifest itself in mental health problems we face as a society, such as addictions and physical illnesses. This is a bold statement to make—that addiction and physical illness are rooted in relational trauma—yet one I totally agree with.

In complex PTSD, clients will repeatedly receive messages that are not aligned with their vulnerable, authentic truth. They disconnect from their Self and internalize the messages they receive. The feelings are often held in their exiled parts, and an elaborate system of protection gets created to protect from the misalignment of their truth and the isolation from their Self. When trauma survivors do receive a message that is aligned with their truth or Self, it's often difficult for them to take it in, as they still hold the belief of a prior assault. Being told "I think you're kind and loving" doesn't ring true to them, and it's hard to receive when they have parts that carry beliefs like "You're worthless," "You're ugly," and "You're unlovable."

One of the main goals in IFS therapy is to help clients reconnect so they can trust their feelings again and regain faith in the Self. For example, when a client says something about me or notices that I'm distracted or tired, I try my best to validate their experience. I'll respond: "Yes, you're correct—my mind did wander just then. Let me take a moment to see if I can get a sense about what's going on for me" or "Yes, you're right. I did react when you told me how I was feeling." Whenever clients are able to speak their truth and we are able to validate their experience, we help them reconnect with their gut feeling, allowing them to trust their inner wisdom again. This trust in Self-leadership, after all, is what was destroyed as a result of the trauma.

Were you accepted for who you are? Were the messages you received aligned with your gut instinct, or did the reaction to your vulnerability present as shaming, critical, or attacking? Relational trauma is about the pain we carry from the perpetrator's reaction to who "they" thought we are, what they thought we should feel, or who they thought we should be. It's the way we're taken advantage of, overpowered, rejected, and alienated that causes the wound. Relational trauma is a violation of healthy loving connection, true intimacy, and the acceptance of our true vulnerable selves.

VULNERABILITY FROM PARTS OR THE SELF?

It's important to differentiate where vulnerability is coming from. Does it originate from the Self or a part? When younger parts express themselves through feelings, beliefs, or physical sensations, there's often an intensity and agenda attached to it.

They're desperate to be seen and heard, and they typically seek redemption from a prior hurt. Unfortunately, when parts express vulnerability in this way, they're likely to activate a part in the other person and reexperience or relive their original hurt. Remember: Parts beget parts. When we respond from a part, we're likely to get a part response in the other. Exiled parts typically don't get the response they're looking for; consequently, the wounds are commonly reinforced. You might very well hear a client's vulnerable wounded part say: "I'm so lonely and afraid. Please stay with me, and promise you'll never leave me."

On the other hand, when vulnerability is expressed from the Self, it is much more likely to get the desired outcome. The Self has an infinitely higher likelihood of getting a corrective or reparative response. Wayne Baker, a dear friend and IFS colleague, says the "Self is the ultimate protector of our vulnerability" (personal communication, September 16, 2019). When we are in Self-energy, our guard drops, our protectors relax, and we can connect to and speak for our feelings and deepest thoughts from a place of strength and power. Here, we are being vulnerable from a place of strength, not desperation. The Self also has better judgment about whom we should share our vulnerability with—whom we can honestly trust versus whom we think can save us.

IFS helps our clients heal from the anguish their parts have endured. We can show our clients the goodness in themselves again and enable them to let go of their perpetrator's harsh words, actions, and beliefs carried by their parts. Trauma makes intimacy and vulnerability seem like a bad idea or scary notion, and the Self helps wounded parts see that they're not the problem after all and begin to experience vulnerability as a strength and a joy, not a weakness or a poor choice. *Trauma blocks self-love, and Self-led vulnerability fosters greater connections and deeper intimacy.*

CHAPTER 15

Reactions to Trauma

COMMON RESPONSES TO RELATIONAL VIOLATIONS

Relational trauma is a violation of our vulnerability, truth in feelings, and trust in the other. A resultant protective cascade evolves in an attempt to keep the sorrow at bay. Here's where therapists spend most of their time: trying to get stubborn or resistant protective parts to relax and allow access to the wounds they're guarding.

Here is a list, not exhaustive by any means, of protective parts that therapists frequently encounter when helping complex PTSD survivors recover:

• Dissociative parts	• Anxious parts
• Suicidal parts	• Critical parts
• Numbing parts	• Vigilant parts
• Shaming parts	• Storytelling parts
• Addictive parts	• Worrying parts
• Passive parts	• Controlling parts
• Perpetrator parts	• Shy parts
• Substance-using parts	• Rigid parts
• Sexually excessive parts	• Rageful or angry parts
• Sexually avoidant parts	• Intellectual parts
• Depressed parts	• Obsessive parts
• Panicked parts	• Conflict-avoidant parts

Next, we'll examine some of the more common protective responses and explore the unique ways these parts interact with each other while protecting their vulnerable counterparts.

DISSOCIATIVE PARTS

As previously discussed in section 3, parts that disconnect, numb out, or remove themselves take on these roles when danger is perceived. Information in the amygdala is redirected from the lateral to the basal nucleus, which activates the ventral striatum;

the PFC becomes overinhibited; and the dorsal parasympathetic nervous system is activated.

I believe that dissociation happens on a spectrum. All of us daydream, occasionally space out, or are overly preoccupied at times, which is at one end of the dissociative spectrum. On the other end of that spectrum are those who constantly leave, lose chunks of time throughout the day, or even split off into discrete identities that function independently and lack awareness of one other. As Dick Schwartz often says, IFS sees dissociation as a part, not as a pathological process.

When I notice dissociation in a client, I might remark: "Emily, I noticed that a part of you just checked out. Are you aware of that? Let's learn more about why that part felt the need to do that." Remember that most dissociative, avoidant, or out-of-here parts aren't particularly interested in engaging in a conversation. Their agenda is to protect by disconnecting, not to converse. The way IFS gets around this is not via grounding techniques, like some other therapies suggest (which is essentially shifting out of one part into another one), but by talking directly to the part and hearing its position. I find this technique more efficient, effective, and respectful to the client's parts.

For example, I might say: "So you're the one who took Emily out a moment ago, is that right?" Waiting for a response, I will often continue the conversation, knowing that it takes dissociative parts a few moments to engage. My next words may be: "I trust that you had a good reason to jump in just then. I suspect that you've needed to do this for quite some time. I'm truly interested in hearing more about that." I'll likely see the client's body gradually shift and slightly soften. This suggests that we've made a connection and can begin a dialogue.

Parts jump in because they feel they have to. Engaging them in conversation allows them to be heard, known, and validated. Grounding strategies, from the IFS perspective, essentially call on another part within the system to show up and override the original part. Here, dissociative parts can feel disregarded or unappreciated. Keep in mind that leaving is often the best solution in a frightening or overwhelming traumatic moment. Instead of getting frustrated and annoyed by these parts, I've grown to love them for their tenacity and persistence.

SUICIDAL PARTS

The extreme example of a part abandoning an untenable situation is suicide. Even though we know in IFS that every part has a positive intention, our profession and culture are programmed to stop it at all costs. I'm aware of the increased suicide rate within the adolescent population at present, which is likely due to the effects of technology and the lack of love, connection, and guidance experienced by this age group. Of course, I'm not in favor of suicide, but I do believe we are approaching it in the wrong way culturally. Sure, we need to differentiate whether or not the suicidal thoughts are connected to a biologically based depression and treat it accordingly. But more importantly, I believe that we need to understand the intentions of these desperate, last-resort parts.

When you're truly able to engage suicidal parts with open-hearted curiosity, you will quickly learn that dying is often the last thing on their minds. *They tend to show up when the pain is high and the access to love is minimal or nonexistent.* Often, these parts are young and don't believe that suicide will lead to their removal. They're the ultimate escape artists. "If it gets bad enough, I have what it takes to stop the pain," is what we hear over and over again from these heroic parts. Appreciate them for the tremendous burden of responsibility they carry for the system.

For therapists to be able to hold this compassionate position, they need to work with their own parts that get activated by these wishes and free themselves from the professional burdens that bind them. It's normal to think things like "It's my job to prevent Hilary from killing herself. If I don't, I've failed, and I will most certainly get sued." When physicians witness clients dying, they usually don't blame themselves when this happens; it's considered a normal aspect of life. Therapists, on the other hand, take on their profession's view and often assume more self-responsibility than is warranted in these situations.

We also need to clear any personal legacy burdens we might carry. For example, my niece accidentally committed suicide a few years back. So every time one of my clients' suicidal parts shows up, I need to keep that part at bay—the one that tries to jump in and convince my client of the potential devastation it would cause for the people in her life. Instead, we all need to take these parts seriously. When we are more sensitive to the significance of their job and the tremendous pain these parts are trying to push away, things tend to go much better; usually, these suicidal parts don't escalate but soften because they finally feel listened to.

The Perpetrator and Passive Parts: Internal Protective Polarities

When a vulnerability is violated and the emotional pain associated with the experience is predominately held in exiled parts, two common protective responses develop independently and in polarization with each other. These are passive parts and perpetrator parts.

Passive parts can be protective and dominate one's life, even though they present as meek, quiet, under the radar, or even hidden. They often run the show from the sidelines. Passive parts can originate directly from exile energy. You may hear them say: "I'm too run-down or beat-up to respond to anyone or anything. I'm helpless." Or they can be protective in nature, remarking: "If I stay quiet, I'm less likely to draw attention to myself and get hurt. Doing nothing is safer than standing out and speaking up. If I stay small, my father won't yell at me."

These parts are physiologically rooted in parasympathetic blunting or withdrawal and tend to activate therapists' parts. Yes, I speak from personal experience here. I can often feel frustrated with a client's seeming lack of motivation to change, their inactivity or inability to mobilize. I may ask questions such as: "Were you able to tell your husband that you'd like to be involved in making decisions about where the family goes on vacation? Were you able to tell your daughter not to talk to you with an abusive tone? Did you inform your boss that you can't work another overnight shift?" No, is the common response I'll hear. My parts get frustrated that the client isn't speaking up, standing up, or even showing up like they probably should, due to the dominance by their passive parts that are working overtime to keep exiled parts out of harm's way. I've had to address the parts of me that get activated by passivity. I now understand that passivity in my history meant that I'd put myself in harm's way. My parts felt the need to act and respond with lightning speed to keep me safe. Being passive was terrifying for them—akin to being a sitting duck in a shooting gallery.

To better illustrate this point, consider the following exchange between me and a client:

> "I'm running out of places to hide," Will said. "I've never really been true to myself, and it constantly blows up in my face. My needs have never mattered, and my regrets are piling up. I only have about 20 years of life left, and I can't keep running like this."

> "I think it's great that you're wanting to make some changes in your life, Will. But let's not throw these parts under the bus just yet. Let's ask them more about their story," I said.

> "They seem to be connected to my drinking part and the way it avoids feelings at all costs too. They seem pretty young," Will said. "I keep hearing 'We can't speak up,' 'It's not allowed,' 'If we talk, then we'll get hit and yelled at even more,' and 'It's not an option for us.'"

> "Let them know that we're hearing what they're saying, Will. It sounds like speaking up was scary for them, and if they did, they clearly would get hurt," I responded.

> "This is making so much sense to me," noted Will. "They learned from a very young age to ignore feelings and never speak up about anything."

> "They had to, Will. It sounds like it was a matter of survival for them," I said.

> "It totally was," Will said, crying quietly.

Some exiled parts learn from a very young age that keeping quiet is a better option than speaking up. This message of passivity is internally imprinted and carries over into adulthood, often getting played out in a myriad of ways. The result is that many complex PTSD survivors remain passive, present as a victim, and are unable or unwilling to speak for their needs. To wit, consider my continued conversation with Will:

> "Will, it's really important that we're learning more about why it's been so hard for you to be true to yourself and to have your needs matter in your adult life. Let these parts know that you're beginning to see why they were so terrified to speak up and that we understand why they needed to keep running away from feelings to stay safe," I said.

"They like that I'm connecting to this. They're saying: 'It's about time,'" Will replied.

"I believe that our feelings are our truth barometers," I said. "They keep us connected to our moral compass and true self. You couldn't do this as a child if you were terrified all the time. You can only know what's true inside when it feels safe enough to do so, and you can only speak up about your emotions and let others have their feelings when the people in charge create the space for that to safely happen."

"I've never even thought about that before," commented Will. "It never seemed possible for me to have my feelings and let them have theirs; that would have been a disaster."

"I believe that was true back then, Will. But if you and I spend time with those younger parts—the ones that needed to disconnect and stay silent to survive—we can help them let go of what they're holding. And you'll be much more capable of doing that now in your life."

"That's hard to believe. But count me in," Will said. "As I said before, I'm running out of time."

Perpetrator parts are also quite prevalent in relational trauma and represent the other side of the polarization. Most trauma survivors incorporate both passive and perpetrator parts, and both tend to be hard to acknowledge and embrace. Perpetrator parts are the parts of the client that take in the energy and effectiveness of the perpetrator. These parts are usually sympathetically activated and hyperaroused. Our clients see and, unfortunately, feel how effective the perpetrator's dominance and power was because they were the recipient of that energy. Young protective parts tend to take on this energy in an attempt to feel big and powerful. Their rationale goes something like this: "Wow, if I attack people as my uncle attacked me, no one will mess with me anymore."

When dealing with perpetrator parts, it's important to differentiate what percentage is the client's part (i.e., that which was internalized) and what percentage is associated with a legacy burden (i.e., energy that belongs to the perpetrator and is attached to the client's system; for more on legacy burdens, see chapter 25). Usually, it's a combination of both the client's part and the perpetrator's energy affixed to the client. The good news here is that both can be released.

An important question to help you differentiate between the two is: "Does this energy inside of you belong to your uncle, or is it yours?" You might hear a response along the lines of: "Forty percent is mine, and the rest belongs to my uncle." A useful response would be: "If this order makes sense to you, let's release the portion that belongs to him first, and then let's help the portion that belongs to you."

Connecting with perpetrator parts can be one of the most painful experiences for trauma survivors. I regularly hear phrases like "I can't believe I did the very thing that was done to me," and I've felt this personally as well when I've yelled at my children as a result of a triggered perpetrator part of me. My internal critic then jumps in and gets extremely harsh toward this angry perpetrator part, admonishing it with statements such as "Look at what you just did. You know better than this. You're a therapist, and you teach appropriate behavior for a living, you jerk."

As difficult as it is sometimes, these perpetrator parts also need to be loved and appreciated for their good intentions, not for their effect. I've learned to appreciate the way my perpetrator part jumps in to protect the young one inside me that gets terrified when my two children fight with each other. I have also become grateful for my internal critic, who works hard to protect my children from my perpetrator's rage.

CRITICAL PARTS

Internal and external critics are commonplace in trauma and are often internalized perpetrator energy that are rooted in some form of judgment or verbal abuse. They excel at hurling insults: "You're going to amount to nothing. You're so damned lazy. You make me sick." Unfortunately, the recipient of these harsh words knows the impact and harm they cause, which can often be felt like an attack on the soul.

However, it's important to help your clients access the intention behind these critical parts. They can be preemptive (a manager) or reactive (a firefighter) in nature and are trying their best to protect your client by getting them to behave, be perfect, not stumble again, or push potential assailants away.

Asking them where they learned to do this job—and if they're interested in discovering a new way of helping—is a relational approach to working with extreme critics that I learned from Chris Burris, a senior lead trainer at the IFS Institute. They typically have a bad reputation in society, in families, and with therapists, which they are well aware of, and when we draw attention to their activity, they inevitably feel shame, which fuels their fire. Again, kindness toward the critic's positive intention goes a long way toward gaining access to the real wound—the one inflicted upon by the original perpetrator, not the well-intended pupil.

Emotions inform our truth and help us stay aligned with what's right for us, which is a textbook description of self-connection. We have no regrets when we connect to what we feel and live and speak our truth. However, in trauma, polarities often form between passive parts and critical parts or perpetrator parts that help push away the pain connected to our overwhelming experiences. One of my clients confessed: "I'm constantly stuck between fighting too hard and never giving up or stepping back and letting everyone else decide for me. I never seem to find the right balance." I assured him that IFS helps resolve these polarizations by joining these sides, appreciating these parts' efforts, and offering to release the anguish they're protecting.

CHAPTER 16

Substance Use: Searching Outside for Protection

It's rare to work with relational trauma and not encounter parts that are connected in some way to an addictive cycle. Many internally damaged systems will look externally for relief, escape, and protection, especially when the internal system has not experienced safety and love early on in life. This is often the case when parts seek solutions to their problems with potentially addictive substances and behaviors, such as food, drugs, sex, technology, and gambling, to name a few. When it comes to these parts, we want to follow the client's internal wisdom about the order of healing. These systems tend to be complex and often have multiple dimensions to them, including facets connected to the past as well as the present. For example, *it's fairly common for there to be more than one substance-using part, and they tend to protect more than one wound.*

Remember that our goal in IFS is not to get the part to stop using their substance of choice; rather, it's to learn about their role, fear, or positive intention and to offer an alternative solution to their problem. This goal nicely aligns with a statement made by Johann Hari in his 2015 TED Talk on addiction: "The opposite of addiction is not sobriety. The opposite of addiction is connection." Be mindful that the overall solution usually involves healing an original wound, commonly rooted in the past, as well as addressing the secondary problems that developed, typically related to circumstances in the present day (as shown in the graphic on the next page).

For example, you may hear a client say: "I'm afraid that if I stop eating, I won't be able to suppress my sexual urges and I'll have another affair," which addresses a problem in the current day. You may also hear the client acknowledge the underlying wound that most likely originated in the past: "I'm afraid that if I stop eating, I'll feel unloved, unimportant, and worthless all over again, just like I did as a kid." Substance-using protective parts often end up protecting an original wound as well as several secondary wounds, some of which develop as a result of the substance itself.

Not only is it common for a substance to protect multiple wounds, but it's also customary for several different parts to be involved in the protective cycle. For example, with sexual addiction, there's often an activated or hyperaroused part that is driven to conquer, be sexual, and achieve the release of orgasm. There is also commonly a restrictive or hypoaroused part that wards off the residual feelings of guilt after a conquest, as well as a part that desperately wants to have a normal sexual connection with someone.

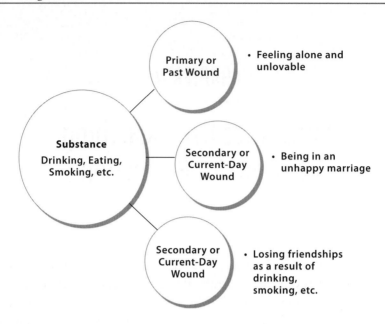

To demonstrate this phenomenon, consider the case of a client named Jon. He had been seeing me for a while, primarily to address his issues with eating that seemed to be related to a contentious divorce with his wife and a history of being bullied at school as a child. Jon would frequently inquire about entering an inpatient program to help him lose weight, something he had struggled with for most of his life. As we began to explore the positive intention of his eating, he quickly discovered that he had many different parts that were organized around food. He identified a part that would "eat to soothe," remembering how he would consume an entire bag of candy bars after being bullied, even though it upset his stomach. Jon also described a "warrior" who would eat to gain strength and have enough fuel to get through the next day at school after an attack. He further described a "last supper" part who ate as much as possible on Sunday night in anticipation of starting a diet the next morning in the hopes that his wife would find him attractive again and stop berating him. Last, Jon named the "mayor," a part who knew how to "take care of everyone in town" and knew what was needed to eat right and live a healthy lifestyle.

When multiple addictive parts get uncovered, don't automatically assume they're all protecting the same wound. Sometimes one part protects more than one wound inside, while at other times, different parts protect various exiles, as was the case with Jon.

Parts, Habits, and Biology

With addictive substances, we help clients identify and heal the underlying wound associated with the protective behavior. But I have come to learn that it's also important to help them address the *habit* and *biological consequences* connected to the substance they're using. We may hear a client say: "I always have a cigarette after I eat and when I drive in the car" (i.e., a habitual behavior) or "How do I safely stop drinking so that I don't go through withdrawal or have a seizure?" (i.e., the biological effect).

I also like to think about the difference between addiction and dependence as they relate to parts, habits, and biology. *Addiction* is defined as compulsive substance use despite potentially harmful consequences and is often accompanied by an inability to stop using it. *Dependence,* on the other hand, occurs when the body adapts to a substance, requiring more of it to achieve the desired affect (i.e., tolerance) and eliciting specific physical or mental symptoms if the drug is abruptly stopped (i.e., withdrawal; National Institute on Drug Abuse, 2020). *I believe protective parts and habits are more often associated with addiction, whereas biology is connected to dependence.*

In most cases, we focus on healing the wound first and secondarily look at changing the habit and addressing biological withdrawal. When I first started working with addictions using IFS, I assumed that healing the wound would spontaneously take care of the habit, as well as the biology. But unfortunately, this was not necessarily the case. Sometimes habits turn out to be protective parts that haven't let go of their job because they weren't informed about an unburdening that took place. Habits can also be entrenched, taking a long time to change, and they may or may not be associated with a protective part.

Having your client ask usually helps to differentiate between a habit and a part. "Jazmin, take a moment and ask inside if any part knows anything about or is connected to your eating dessert after dinner." Jazmin responded: "The part says it usually starts out eating to get away from stressful or overwhelming feelings, but at night, the habit kicks in and just keeps eating." When parts are uncertain or don't take responsibility for the behavior, it's likely a habit. In addition, withdrawing from some addictive substances (i.e., addressing biology) may require the support of a medical specialist to taper safely and to help prevent distressing or dangerous side effects.

Again, it's important to address all of the facets associated with the substance in question. Is food restriction connected to a protective part that's trying to prevent an exile from feeling unloved? Is it associated with a habit? (Statements like "Ever since college, I stopped eating breakfast and lunch" or "I was always so busy; it just became part of my normal routine" can confirm this.) Or is it a symptom of decreased appetite that is related to a biological depression?

Trust the client's internal wisdom regarding the order they assign to addressing the habit and biology. One of my clients was clear that he needed to decrease his alcohol intake before he was able to honestly address feelings connected to his retirement. Another client had a part of her that didn't trust her Self enough yet—a part that wanted her to "walk the talk." It requested that she first start exercising and enter Weight Watchers before it would trust her enough to access the feelings of inadequacy. Yet another client of mine was able to unburden the little boy inside of him who was raped by his uncle as a child. As his exile started feeling the love and kindness it was robbed of by his uncle, his system decided to enter an outpatient eating-disorder program to address some of the residually embedded behaviors that were still present in his life.

In IFS, as it relates to the addictive process and trauma, we explore all the different parts that are connected to the substance at hand. We also examine the various wounds underneath the parts. Further, it's important to address the habits, rituals, routines, addictions, or cravings that have been established around each particular substance and to help the client develop a plan for addressing them. We also consider dependence or the biological realities of each substance and help our clients safely decrease using the substance when the timing is right for the system.

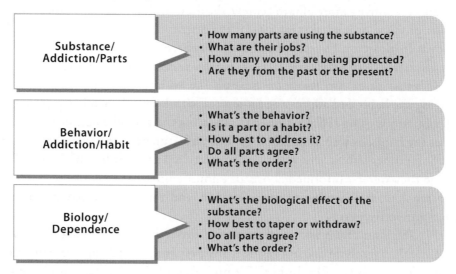

To demonstrate IFS's efficacy here, consider the case of my client Rebecca. After working with Rebecca's pot-smoking part for several sessions in a row, she was able to acknowledge the consequences of the part's behavior:

"I know that it's dangerous to drive our boat when I'm stoned. My wife gets on my case, especially when the kids are on board," Rebecca told me. "My pot-smoking part really likes to be seen by me; it feels my love and support. She's willing to rein it in. She says my love gives her the strength to try and cut down."

Rebecca then got misty-eyed and noted: "Wow, I just realized the connection—that I've been smoking for years because I never felt loved by my parents growing up. They were so caught up in their own stuff that I never felt their love."

At this point, I offered the invitation: "Rebecca, let the pot-smoking part know that we can help heal the younger part that didn't feel loved."

"Oh, my goodness, it's like I'm getting this for the first time," Rebecca replied. "When I love the pot-smoking part, she feels that love and her heart opens up, which allows me in turn to love my wife and kids even more. She wants to stop smoking because she also loves them and doesn't want to do anything that would put them in harm's way."

Rebecca made an important connection, followed by asking these crucial questions: "Healing involves connecting to the goodness in all of us. It involves love, even for our parts. The pot-smoking part can block love, needs love, and can even offer love, right?"

"Absolutely," I responded, as I started to get teary-eyed.

Associated Parts: Critics, Caretakers, and Thinkers

When addressing parts that use substances in the service of protection, there's often a host of related parts that get activated in connection to the wound. These are critical or shaming parts, caretaking parts, and parts that intellectualize or tell the story. This grouping of parts makes it much more challenging to receive permission to access the wound. For example, addictive parts will feel bad about their behavior and the trouble they've caused, both internally (to the system) as well as externally (to the people around them). It's common for internal critics to show up and shame the addictive part for its behavior too.

Some parts caretake and desperately try to please, fix the problem, and offer guidance in the service of keeping the pain away. There are also those unrelenting parts that hold the story and remain in place, attempting to think and figure things out. These parts are notorious for having a hard time unblending and providing space, but persistence, patience, and compassion usually pay off in the end.

CHAPTER 17

Shame Cycles Associated with Trauma

With complex relational trauma, shame is ubiquitous and becomes a complicated system unto itself. When we're vulnerable, connected to our truth in feeling, or connected to our power and someone reacts harshly or responds to us in an abusive way, they sever our Self-connection. Additionally, they activate or help create parts in us that hold or carry feelings of worthlessness, self-loathing, or being "less than." Thoughts like "I'm bad," "I'm wrong," or "I must be the problem" emerge.

Remember: *Shame develops when vulnerability is relationally violated.* In other words, shame is the anti-Self or the opposite of love and connection. Once during a session, an intuitive client told me: "When shame dominates, trauma wins. It gets in the way of me being me. It blocks me from being able to do what I'm capable of. When I believe the bad, I block the love I have for myself and the others in my life." Truer words were never spoken, proving that we can often learn more from our clients than they can from us.

There are two shame cycles I commonly, though not exclusively, come across as a result of repeated relational betrayal. One originates from parental or authority figures who frequently engage with children from a critical or verbally abusive part. The other comes from caregivers who respond from a part of themselves who is neglectful or abandoning of others. The critical parts in caregivers are typically harsh, hyperaroused, or sympathetically activated, while the neglectful, abandoning parts are more often parasympathetically blunted. Both represent triggered or blended states within the caregiver.

CRITICAL SHAME CYCLES

Growing up in a critical, strict, verbally abusive environment will often produce an exile that holds shame and feels unworthy, bad, or unlovable as a result of the damaging words it has absorbed from a parent or bully. The negative feelings that result are predictable, with clients telling themselves "I'm rotten" or "I'm worthless." Being verbally abused not only produces an exile who carries shame, but it also produces a verbally abusive *internal critic*. Similar to the origin of perpetrator parts (chapter 15), this critical part typically originates in one of two ways: (1) it can become a part of the client that takes on the energy of the critical person in their life, or (2) it can represent the external person's energy that affixes to the client's system but is not necessarily a part of the client per se. Again, we refer to the latter as a legacy burden.

When the internal critic is a part of the client, it adopts a protective function. It often becomes critical of other parts within the client's system in an attempt to get them to "shape up and stop their bad behavior" in the hopes that the shamed exile won't get activated again. Common critical thoughts are "Your eating is the reason people hate us. If you stop, they won't make fun of us anymore" and "What's wrong with you—it's so obvious, don't you get that?"

Other protective parts also commonly show up as a result of being in a verbally abusive environment. There is often a *substance-using part* that tries to soothe the pain, a *pleasing or trying-to-be-perfect part* that attempts to fix the problem by getting people to like them, and a *disconnecting part* that says: "I'm out of here. I'll leave (dissociate) or even kill us all if things get bad enough."

To complicate things even further, each of these protective parts within the system self-perpetuates the shame cycle because they *feel bad about their own behavior.* They foster shaming thoughts, such as "I know my drinking keeps causing a great deal of pain to my family," "I keep trying to get people to like me, but I'm constantly failing," or "I know that leaving all the time pushes away the people I love the most." Here, shame begets more shame. These protective parts, which try to prevent the shamed wound from being triggered, are often ashamed of their behavior. The internal critic part often feels the worst of all, as it knows better than most how painful it is to be the recipient of criticism.

In my experience, there's nothing worse than being aware that you're perpetrating in a similar way that you've been perpetrated upon. Some of the worst moments in my life involve raising an angry voice to someone, just as I was yelled at in my childhood.

Note that, as the therapist, pointing out the effect of this vicious cycle can inject more shame into the client's system. It is our job to compassionately create a space of gentle exploration without judgment, to help these parts unload the shame they carry toward themselves and the other parts within the system they have shamed. Here is a diagram of a critical shame cycle produced by an external verbally abusive critic.

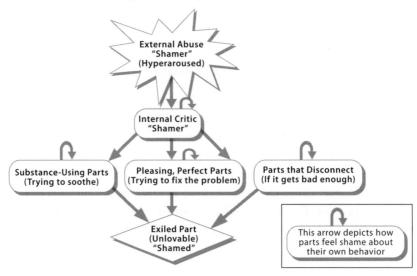

As you can see, this is a very intricate and convoluted cycle that perpetuates and reinforces shame produced by a critical outsider. In her best-selling book *Daring Greatly*, Brené Brown states that "shame is the fear of disconnection" and that "we are psychologically, emotionally, cognitively, and spiritually hard-wired for connection, love, and belonging" (2012, p. 68). She further adds that "shame is the intensely painful feeling or experience of believing that we are flawed and therefore unworthy of love and belonging" (2012, p. 69). I believe her definitions describe many of the exiles we work with in IFS, especially when we treat clients who have repeatedly been relationally criticized. The key takeaway here? *Shame is one of the primary wounds created when our vulnerability is attacked.*

NEGLECT SHAME CYCLES

When children repeatedly encounter parental neglect, deprivation, or abandonment, they can feel ashamed and alone. This results from a lack of interest, love, and connection from the people they hold dear and rely on the most. It's easy for kids to personalize this disinterest and feel unlovable, unworthy, and awful about themselves.

I like how Ken Benau describes this type of shame: "To seek special care and love when we are hurting and to have those needs met is to know, without words, that we are both loved and 'good.' To repeatedly not have our desire for care met, particularly when we are most vulnerable, is deeply shaming…. *Care sought and unmet is shaming*" (Benau, 2019).

Bessel van der Kolk states that human contact and attunement are the wellsprings of physiological self-regulation, and the promise of closeness often evokes fear of getting hurt, betrayed, and abandoned when shame is involved (van der Kolk, 2014). He further explains that unresolved trauma can take a terrible toll on relationships. For instance, if you were assaulted by someone you loved, you are likely to be preoccupied with not getting hurt again and fear opening up to someone new. You may try to hurt them before they have a chance to hurt you (van der Kolk, 2014).

This shame cycle is typically caused by a disconnected, hypoaroused, or withdrawn part of the primary caregiver. It, too, produces a typical range of protective responses within the child in an attempt to protect itself from and avoid the pain of shame and isolation held within the exile. Commonly, an *internalized numb or disconnected part* in the child uses disconnection to escape—a coping mechanism it likely learned from the parent. With the resultant lack of connection, there's often space inside that's filled up by an *intellectual part* trying to understand why a parent doesn't love or care about them. These intellectual parts are often steadfast and have a hard time stepping back and giving room. Remember, "too much space" is problematic for these parts, and giving more space only perpetuates the loneliness.

There are also *perfectionistic parts* that commonly show up and try to solve the old problem of being unwanted by being perfect in the present. Unfortunately, they use outdated or immature behaviors, are often intense, and can come across as judgmental, angry, and frightening when they take over. Again, these parts, by the nature of their behavior, will produce more internalized shame.

There's also the *out-of-here part* to reckon with, the one that thinks: "We've never been loved and never will be. What's the point? It's hopeless. I'm out of here." In this shame cycle that emerges from abandonment and neglect, feelings are often extremely difficult to access. The client's parts are driven by the absence of unmet needs for love, care, and connection. What they know is nothing! Therefore, accessing emotion is generally foreign to these clients. As a result, it's also difficult for them to take in love when it does show up.

Below is a diagram demonstrating the cycle of shame that originates from neglect.

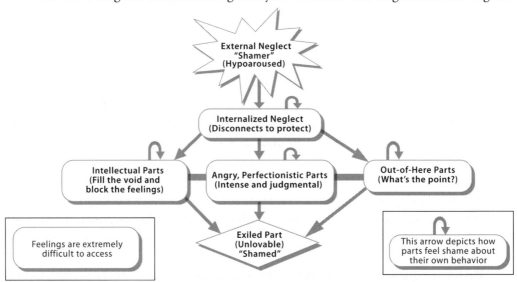

Shame is not only confined to these two scenarios—one originating from critical verbal abuse and the other from neglect—but it's often at the core of most complex trauma wounding. The resulting experience of isolation, feeling unworthy and unlovable, and not being seen is physiologically profound and at the core of most shame experiences. We've all felt shame at various times in our lives. But our resourceful protective parts build up elaborate and sophisticated systems to help us avoid life-threatening experiences of shame.

Bullying has been prevalent in our culture for so long, and school systems have thankfully started to acknowledge the damaging effects it can have on children. The exiled parts that hold shame are prime targets for being bullied by others. Likewise, the protective parts that develop as a result of being bullied are prime candidates for becoming bullies themselves or for alternatively stopping the pain at all costs through suicide. Unfortunately, many people have been on both sides of this fence, and it's important to be mindful that at the core of shame is a feeling of being alone and unlovable—yet another example of trauma blocking love.

Ponder, for a moment, the case of Susan, a bright and emotionally intelligent graduate student who came to see me because she felt it was time to work on some childhood issues before starting a family. She was in a long-term relationship that seemed surprisingly stable considering what she had experienced in her youth. Susan had spent time in a religious community that had dismantled about 10 years prior, after several of its members disclosed sexual abuse at the hands of one of the leaders.

Fortunately, Susan had not been abused, but she described the environment as "having an aura of self-righteousness that attracted wounded healers. Everyone was told that we were there because we were 'chosen,' and if we connected to the divine daily through prayer, ate healthy, never partook in alcohol or drugs, and fully committed to the leader, we would be enlightened in short order. So I worked diligently to achieve this goal. When I messed up—let's say I ate ice cream, snuck a hamburger, or skipped a morning meeting—I felt horrible and frequently would cut myself to get some relief from the pain and to punish myself for what I had done. I knew I wasn't living up to the ideal of the leader and, once again, had failed. I imagined that I was a huge disappointment to him. Being there reminded me of my family of origin. I could never live up to their standards either and constantly felt like a failure growing up as a child. Here, I was doomed to be a total disappointment all over again."

As Susan and I explored the origins of her inner critic, we learned that, much to her surprise, two different parts of her produced shame. One part originated from her mother's harsh and punitive words—this was the part of Susan that believed in embracing physical harm through cutting. The other part came from her father; it was absolute in its thinking, either being "totally right" or "knowing absolutely nothing at all." Susan added that she felt "like I'm constantly on a roller-coaster ride or I have bipolar disorder or something." We learned that this part of her was young, around 5 or 6 years old, and developed as a result of her father's absence. He often traveled for work, and this part of her felt alone and believed that it had to learn things by itself.

When I said that it must have been hard for that little girl to be criticized by her mother and abandoned by her father, Susan instantly agreed. I also shared with her that kids often feel responsible for the way they were treated and asked her to explore if any parts felt at fault. That's when she burst into tears. She was able to connect compassionately for the first time with both of her critical parts, and she was also capable of appreciating the little girl who felt shamed by them, worthless, and utterly alone. "I see what a huge influence those parts of me have had over my life, both as a little girl and also as an adult in my church community," she remarked. "I'm so glad we're getting to the bottom of this because I don't want to pass any of this down to my children."

Susan had a parent who was more activated and critical, and another parent who was absent and unavailable—each producing different shaming cycles within her system. Unfortunately, this is a more common occurrence than you think, and these shame systems are often deeply embedded and difficult for clients to unblend from. I believe that clients who are labeled as having borderline personality disorder or who struggle with disorganized attachment often have parents with parts that are harsh and verbally abusive and/or parts that are blunted, neglectful, or abandoning. Both extremes produce shamed exiles in those they interact with, and it's much more toxic when they coexist together.

As the therapist, it is our job to compassionately hold the space for gentle exploration and to help each part unload the shame it carries toward itself and other parts within the system. If we directly point out these cycles to clients, we become part of the problem instead of the solution. And we inject even more shame into an already shame-ridden system.

THE NEUROSCIENCE OF SHAME

An article summarizing the literature on the neurobiological underpinnings of shame found that shame is likely associated with activity in the dorsolateral PFC, posterior cingulate cortex, and sensorimotor cortex (Bastin et al., 2016). Louis Cozolino also describes how the freeze response represents a rapid transition from sympathetic activation to parasympathetic inhibition and that, with shame, children are snapped from a mode of curiosity, exploration, and excitement (mild sympathetic arousal) to one of shutdown and withdrawal (dorsal parasympathetic blunting). He also explains that these "mini traumas" stimulate the same regions of the brain that are activated during pain (Cozolino, 2014). In other words, shame is associated with parasympathetic withdrawal, and we feel it in our body the same way we experience something physically painful.

To demonstrate this point, reflect on John, another client of mine. John was a very successful, high-powered lawyer who came to see me because he wasn't having enough sex with his wife, wanted to lose some weight, and yearned to get in better shape. I was impressed that he even sought my help because, in my experience, these types of men generally don't want to talk about their feelings. But there was something different about John, and as he began to tell me his history several red flags popped up that indicated there was more to his story.

On the surface, John was bright and accomplished. He was at the top of his law school class, ran a successful practice, and had a beautiful wife and three happy and healthy children. He was highly intellectual, but occasionally during our sessions he would utter revealing statements like "I hate myself," "When I fasted for a month in college…," "I got beat up in school," and "When my mother was hospitalized for months at a time…" When I heard one of these curious truths emerge, I would pause and encourage John to elaborate and examine that statement. However, John would resist, preferring to only offer facts and stay disconnected from any emotion. John once told me his wife thought he was incapable of feeling, which made me think that John was detached from his feelings on one level, but on another level, there were glimpses of something darker and deeper lurking under the surface.

Over time, John's intellectual part began to trust him and me more. We were able to learn about his perfectionistic part, which was active toward himself as well as his children. We learned about his exercising and eating parts and their drive to help him achieve his goal weight. We discovered his defensive parts that would often hear feedback as criticism and do their best to make John be seen in a positive light, no matter what. And we identified his suicidal part that would never let him experience the depression he felt in grade school after he was bullied, choosing instead to insist: "If we get depressed again, I'm out of here. I'll kill myself for sure."

Slowly, we began to recognize the hurt and pain these parts were protecting. John was constantly criticized by his father and could never live up to his ideal. These parts yearned for unconditional love. We uncovered the early attachment wounds he suffered when his mother was frequently hospitalized for depression. Family members told him that his mother was hospitalized for more than three months after he was born, and his father frequently left him alone in the crib crying to "teach him how to fall asleep on his own." To this day, John still goes to sleep holding his "special pillow" like a stuffed animal.

I will never forget the look on John's face when I asked if he was aware of any parts that may be carrying shame. At that moment, it was as if all his pain had been named for the first time. As we slowly continued to heal the wounds he carried, John's life began to transform in wonderful and surprising ways. His exercising part took up yoga, while his intellectual part began reading about astronomy—a subject John was never able to pursue due to his need to achieve. He is more honest and emotional with his wife and children, to whom he can now talk about his needs and say no without fear of betrayal or abandonment.

The lesson to be learned here? *Shame is at the root of most relational wounds born from criticism, verbal abuse, abandonment, neglect, and physical and sexual abuse.*

On the next page is a blank template you and your clients can use to keep track of their unique shame cycles.

How Science Values Parts

In addition to the research on empathy and compassion, Tania Singer and her lab have conducted important research using the IFS concept of parts and have shown that people who are able to identify and connect with their parts are better able to know another person's perspective and mental state, also known as theory of mind (Böckler et al., 2017). Put another way, the better we understand ourselves, the greater we are able to accurately comprehend the intentions and beliefs of others.

Her endeavor was called the ReSource Project, which examined 332 participants who completed three distinct mental training modules. One, the "presence module," focused on cultivating present-moment attention and interoceptive awareness (body awareness). The second, the "affect module," focused on socioaffective qualities of care, compassion, gratitude, and prosocial motivation. The third, the "perspective module," modeled after IFS, focused on sociocognitive abilities, such as metacognition and perspective taking, on the Self and others (Böckler et al., 2017). The latter module produced the most robust findings of the three groups, especially when people were able to identify negatively balanced parts of themselves.

Dick Schwartz says that accepting previously unacceptable parts of yourself and others plays a central role in therapeutic success (Schwartz, 2013), which is one of the central tenets of the IFS model. This corroborates what Singer and her group found. Singer states that "an increasingly complex and interconnected world where taking the view of others, especially those from different cultures or different religious backgrounds, becomes ever more difficult and ever more necessary" (Böckler et al., 2017, p. 207).

I believe that IFS is perfectly positioned to be that vehicle of change in the world, and Singer's research supports this. To be more tolerant and accepting of ourselves and others, even those who are different from us, is what the world desperately needs right now.

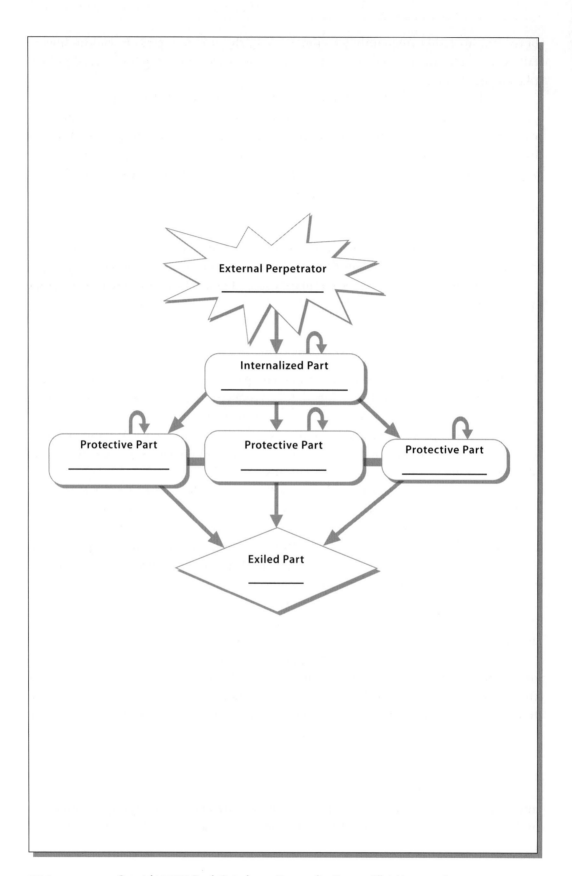

SECTION VI

Associated Features of Trauma

CHAPTER 18

Systems, Severe Trauma, and Polarities

IDENTIFYING COMPLICATED SYSTEMS

The constellation of parts (i.e., systems formed around repeated relational trauma) tends to be complicated, confusing, and often undiscovered for quite some time. It's even more pronounced and perplexing with clients who suffer from dissociative disorders. However, consistent patterns tend to emerge within these complex systems if you're open to discovering them and allow them to unfold accordingly.

For example, there is often a *series of extreme parts*, including suicidal, destructive, critical, cutting, and substance-using parts. There are also several *very strong managers* that can run the client's day-to-day life. Deep inside, often out of the client's conscious awareness, lie the *hidden exiles*. These exiles can be singular, such as a "little Jane" who carries multiple traumas over time, including being yelled at by her mom, violated by boys in the neighborhood, and bullied at school.

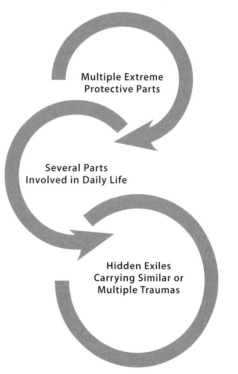

Multiple Extreme Protective Parts

Several Parts Involved in Daily Life

Hidden Exiles Carrying Similar or Multiple Traumas

There can also be multiple exiles that carry similar trauma over time, such as being sexually abused by a brother at 4, 10, and 13 years old. Or there can be multiple exiles holding multiple traumas that are organized within an elaborate, interconnected system (e.g., a 4-year-old who witnessed parental fighting, an 8-year-old traumatized by sibling bullying, and a 13-year-old holding on to abuse by an uncle).

The diagram here shows how these complex systems interrelate.

Consider the following case example. I worked with my client, Martha, for several years on her issues with DID. We spent most of our time getting to know the numerous parts of her that dominated Martha's life. There was a suicidal part that didn't care whether she lived or died, a cutting part that only cut in hidden areas of her body, a part that went to work and managed over 50 employees in her department, a part that hated her husband, a part that went to visit her verbally abusive sister weekly, a part that was raped in college, a part that liked to do puzzles, a part that felt numb, a part that ran the house and managed the kids, a part that became manic, a part that was jealous of her son's success, and an anxious part that jumped in every time Martha felt overwhelmed. And this was only a small sample of Martha's many parts.

Most sessions were spent interviewing these parts, either through insight or direct access. Slowly, over time, I began to notice that certain parts were consistently mentioned together. They started coalescing into groups. For example, the part that ran the house, the anxious part, the cutting part, and the suicidal part would often show up together. Meanwhile, the parts that were angry at Martha's husband, were jealous of her son, got manic, numbed her out, visited her sister, and enjoyed completing puzzles often came together too.

As I started sharing these groupings with Martha, she was well aware of the fact that they were connected but was never forthcoming with this information. She also was reluctant to share whom these groups were protecting. "Sharing that information would make me vulnerable, and I don't do vulnerable," Martha told me. I didn't push back, but I always held this information about Martha's different systems in the back of my mind. It felt like I was putting together a giant jigsaw puzzle mostly by myself. Every once in a while, I would get another piece of the puzzle when we interviewed one of her parts. As shown below, after working together for about two-and-a-half years, we

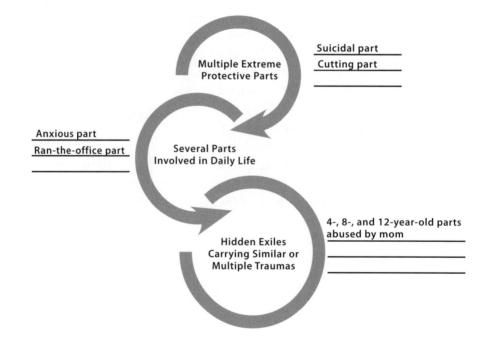

learned that the anxious, cutting, suicidal, and hard-working parts were all protecting three little exiles: those stuck in ages 4, 8, and 12. These parts held on to the sexually inappropriate things Martha's mother would do to her when she was drunk.

We also learned that the parts that were angry at her husband, jealous of her son, manic, numbed out, enjoyed puzzles, and visited her sister were protecting a little girl who felt alone and unloved by her father.

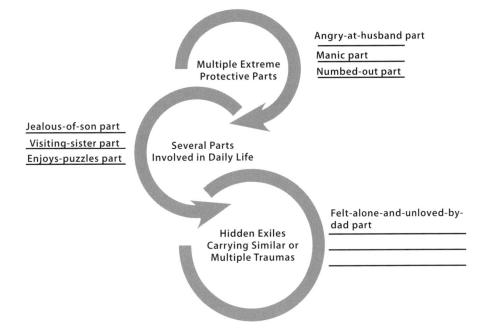

With dissociative disorders, protectors are often part of an elaborate system, reluctant to separate, slow to trust, and hesitant to reveal whom they're protecting. It can take months to years before you and your clients get a sense of who is protecting what. In the early stages of treatment, it's common to engage in *implicit direct access* with the myriad of protectors that show up in your clients. Here, we talk in general to them, attempt to get to know them, and begin to see how they relate to one another and interact within the system as a whole.

Be mindful that some protective parts in dissociative systems are reluctant to be seen and known, so calling them out too soon can be problematic. However, over time, as they begin to feel safe and more at ease, switching to *explicit direct access* is often an essential strategy in getting to know their job, learning about their fears, and gaining parts' permission to access the wound they're protecting. You may also need to offer *the invitations* (as discussed in chapter 9) hundreds of times before they are truly willing to allow the Self to be in connection with the exile. Remember, it can be a single exile holding many traumas, several exiles holding similar painful events, or several exiles holding different but related experiences. Being patient is the key to solving and, ultimately, healing these complex puzzles.

Here is a blank template you can use to map out complicated systems within your clients.

Multiple Extreme Protective Parts

_____
_____
_____

Several Parts Involved in Daily Life

_____
_____
_____

Hidden Exiles Carrying Similar or Multiple Traumas

_____
_____

JOINING THE SYSTEM

As we can see, systems that develop as a result of trauma can be intricate, elaborate, and sometimes convoluted. When we see clients over a long span, it's easy to inadvertently slip or get indoctrinated into their belief system. With complex trauma, there's often a desperation or futility that ensues within the system, especially after many parts have been trying to solve a problem unsuccessfully for years, which they realize. They're generally not open to new ideas and tend to slowly convince therapists about what happened and what will happen.

Make no mistake: Therapists can get brainwashed by parts and begin to buy into their beliefs. You may find yourself thinking: "Maybe nothing will ever significantly change for Samantha," "Perhaps Ava doesn't have enough Self-energy to ever fully recover from her rape," "It's possible Theo is better off living alone," or "Maybe IFS doesn't work for this client."

Consider the case of Jody, a long-term client of mine who had a horrible trauma history that included a schizophrenic mother and an alcoholic father who worked as a traveling salesperson. Jody's early attachment history was anything but secure. She worked hard in therapy to try to have healthy adult relationships, despite her upbringing. I would have probably diagnosed Jody with dissociative disorder not otherwise specified (DDNOS) before my IFS training. She didn't have distinct shifts from one part to another but would subtly and almost seamlessly move in and out of parts without much notice.

Jody would frequently get discouraged and blame me for her lack of progress in therapy as well as in her life. "This therapy isn't helping me," I would often hear her say. "I've spent so much money here over the years, and what do I have to show for it? Nothing. You're supposedly so well-known. You should be good at this stuff. Why aren't you helping me get better? I need someone who cares about me as a person, not someone who travels all the time and writes books."

After one of these episodes, I would feel inadequate and alternate between thinking that Jody either lacked the capacity to heal or that I lacked the skills she needed to guide that healing. My supervision group helped me see that I was getting indoctrinated into Jody's system of hopelessness. I began to examine my parts that were believing Jody's parts. What was striking was that I wasn't feeling these emotions with any other clients or in any other areas of my life.

I became aware of a part of me that didn't like being blamed for Jody's struggles and another younger part that would constantly try to fix her problems. It was a relief to be able to identify these parts within me and appreciate the ways they slowly became integrated into Jody's system. I was able to unblend from these parts and reject responsibility for her complaints about me. As a result, our work shifted pretty dramatically. I was able to embody more objectivity and compassion while Jody began to understand and own her feelings more fully. She was even able to identify a thought-disordered part that internalized her mother's projections and distortions of her as a child. Jody ultimately decided to take a low-dose antipsychotic medication, which made a huge difference in our work together and in her ability to connect with others with less suspicion and more vulnerability.

We often inevitably and dangerously get drawn into a client's system. This is a result of our parts being subconsciously willing to join in a belief that the client's parts subliminally suggest. The challenge here is to remain within the IFS framework, stay the course, and not buy into the opinion or stance of the client's system. *We need to feel confident enough to challenge these beliefs, extricate ourselves from them, unblend from our activated parts, and convince the client's parts that there's another way to see this and resolve this problem.* Using the right language can help immensely: "I know you're feeling hopeless right now, but my perspective is that you can get beyond what happened to you when you were younger. I know you feel incapable of feeling any love in your life right now, but I know it's possible for you. If your parts permit us, we can heal the part of you that believes you are not capable of loving someone."

These hopeless parts tend to block progress from the inside out. They are firmly entrenched in their beliefs and work hard to convince us that their story is true. Once we remove ourselves from the client's system, we can gain firsthand experience of the nature of their pain and the difficulty and hopelessness the system feels. We can then compassionately and effectively rise above it, challenge the story, and separate ourselves from the ubiquitous nature of their experience. When we get drawn into our client's pessimistic stories, it's important to monitor our parts and trust in the healing capacity of Self-energy and the effectiveness of the IFS model. Always remember: We can help our clients heal, even if their tenacious belief system is convinced that it's not possible.

At times, it's helpful to join their system and experience what they feel firsthand. At times, it's necessary to step back, challenge any misleading and malformed beliefs, and suggest how they can unload the hurt and free themselves from carrying the burden of their experiences.

I can now see how my own trauma history and misguided parts have caused me to get sucked into my clients' systems at times—either by carrying too much of their pain, trying too hard to understand or figure things out without seeing the big picture, or tolerating too much and not setting appropriate limits.

DISSOCIATIVE IDENTITY DISORDER

Clients with more severe abuse histories that include ongoing sexual, physical, and verbal abuse seem to have a wide range of parts, both extreme and preventive, that dominate most of their sleeping and waking hours. These parts have a difficult time relaxing enough for Self-energy to emerge. This has been an ongoing source of frustration and confusion for me over the years with many of my clients who struggle with DID.

I have often heard Dick Schwartz say that when parts step back, the Self will naturally emerge. In my heart, I know this to be true. But with many of my clients who have DID, this is not always the case. Some clients seem to have an extremely hard time accessing Self-energy. It's easy for me to become frustrated with myself and wonder: "What am I doing wrong? Why can't I help my client achieve what Dick says to be true?" At other times, parts of me get frustrated with my clients and their seeming lack of capacity to be able to access Self-energy. I find myself wondering: "This must be one of the exceptions to Dick's rule. Is the problem me and my lack of skill, or is it the client and their lack of capacity?"

For clients with DID, in particular, it can feel like a "parts festival" as clients constantly shift from one extreme part to another. And if by chance a Self-like manager shows up, it's easy to get fooled into thinking that the Self is finally present. Hence, you follow the model's steps only to become disappointed when things don't proceed as you know they should. It's quite common for clients who struggle with dissociative disorders to have *highly sophisticated Self-like parts*. They've needed to develop parts that can show up and interact in the world. These parts have carefully observed people and figured out how to fit into society. They're very convincing and often trick therapists into believing they are the Self.

One of the ways to determine if the Self or a Self-like part is present is to ask your client directly: "Is the compassion coming from your head or your heart?" This will help the client differentiate between the two and enable them to begin to sense what the Self feels like internally. Over time, you will get more proficient at identifying the openness and will sense the softening and body relaxation that accompanies Self-energy in your clients. You'll also become more adept at detecting Self-energy in others once you've developed a comfort knowing what it feels like within yourself.

Hallmark symptoms of DID, as they relate to IFS, include the *number, frequency, and intensity of polarized parts* present at any one time. It's not only a parts festival—it's also a polarization bonanza. One part is conflicted with another part that's in opposition with a different part and so on. Sometimes I'm convinced that my clients with DID leave my office and say silently to themselves: "Yes, we've just confused the hell out of him again. Mission accomplished." If protective parts can keep us confused, frightened, and overwhelmed by the intensity, severity, impulsivity, and complexity of their presentation, they feel successful yet again at keeping the vulnerability at bay. It's a brilliant way to stay away from trauma feelings and memories if you stop and think about it.

Clients with DID will also have several parts that *collude with each other*, form packs, and present like a well-orchestrated magic show. They continually lie, hide, and distort the truth, and they are often reluctant to reveal anything about their colluding compatriots. For proof, ponder the following conversation I once had with a client's teenage part:

"Do you know about the part that calls itself 'fear baby'?" I asked.

"Yes, of course I do," it replied.

"Well, that's news to me," I said, trying to keep my frustrated parts at bay. "Is anyone else in there hiding or lying right now?"

A 9-year-old part spoke up and said: "I've been hiding for a while, and I lied when you asked if we were ever bullied by my sister."

It's important to not take the lying and withholding personally; remember this behavior is in the service of protection.

Working with clients who have DID can often feel like a roller-coaster ride. You experience a series of ups and downs with extreme hyperaroused and numbing dissociative parts that switch back and forth at what feels like the speed of light. You feel like you're constantly *chasing one crisis after another*, never fully having a sense as to what is going on inside of your client's mind. I've come to understand that this is the point: Protective parts want to keep you and your client confused and guessing so exiled parts remain out of conscious awareness and unexposed in any way.

Parts can initially *present symbolically* or in an array of nonhuman forms—for example, as a fire-breathing dragon, a dark smoky figure, a cackling witch, fog, a boulder, a locked safe, or a brick wall. As the relationship develops between a part and the Self, they typically, but not always, transform into human form. Staying open, without judgment or agenda, will allow the part to evolve as it sees fit. You may also notice that clients with DID often display *rapid eye movements* when they're thinking about something or retreating inward. I often see this and wonder what's going on inside their head, knowing that a very small percentage ever gets spoken aloud to me.

Therapists need to learn, mostly through experience, to ride out the waves in a nonreactive, matter-of-fact manner so that the client's system realizes you won't get flustered by all the drama. Protectors will naturally begin to relax and trust you as their tour guide through the healing journey. Remember that clients who struggle with DID often have parts that *hate the Self* and have no interest in getting to know it. They'll need to trust you before they're willing to trust the one who, in their eyes, betrayed them and left them behind to endure the torture. *The Self can initially appear weak and marginally accessible* in clients who struggle with DID, but over time it becomes more consistent, dependable, and readily available as parts get to know it better and develop a secure relationship with it.

Know that IFS therapy with clients who have DID is essentially the same as it is with other trauma survivors, but it tends to be more challenging, activate more parts of the therapist, and involve more extreme symptoms, and it takes much longer to help clients access Self-energy, get permission from protectors, and heal or unburden wounds.

> **Clients with DID**
>
> - **Numerous parts, many of them extreme**
> - **Highly evolved Self-like parts**
> - **Multiple polarizations**
> - **Parts that collude and form alliances**
> - **Parts that hide, exaggerate, or are dishonest**
> - **Crisis-driven systems**
> - **Parts that present symbolically**
> - **Rapid eye movements are common**
> - **Parts often hate the Self**
> - **The Self is marginally accessible**

The Invisible Injuries of Neglect

Neglect, in some way, can be as challenging as DID. These systems tend to be steadfast, rock-solid, and unwavering in their attempt to keep the lack of love and connection permanently hidden. There's a desperation to fill the void with something that keeps the feeling of isolation away. As previously discussed, protective parts associated with neglect injuries often show up in the form of thinking, analyzing, figuring out, and perfectionism. They're commonly part of a shame cycle. They can be pervasive within the system and tenacious in their reluctance to step back or separate, thinking: "Why would I step back? If I do, there will be nothing there." I often see these *highly intellectualized manager parts and perfectionistic parts as staunch protectors of neglect.*

As you review your caseload, evaluate how many of your clients with neglect histories have strong storytelling, obsessive, or intellectualized parts. I see them as heroes working around the clock to ward off a wound they can't see, feel, or touch. I have found that working from the bottom up—focusing first on the body, then the emotions, and last the thoughts—can be an entry point to help some of these parts begin to separate.

Parts that protect by discussing, figuring out, and understanding often think they are the Self. But speaking from personal experience, it's relatively easy to differentiate them from Self-energy. That's because I can get bored, distracted, and disinterested in these parts as they ramble on about the details of their narrative. It's also common to feel ineffective with these parts after several unsuccessful attempts to help them separate and allow the Self to emerge. Several of my long-term clients are those who have wounds rooted in neglect. They stay in connection with me for years, with several parts of them clinging to an external connection because they're void of an internal one. These clients have a difficult time accessing Self-energy and struggle to complete a full unburdening.

Clients with neglect-driven systems have a *difficult time connecting with what they feel and struggle with making decisions.* Under normal circumstances, we use a combination of our thoughts, feelings, and intuitive sense to make a decision (i.e., a combination of our parts and the Self): "This makes sense to me. It feels right. I'm going to do it." Clients who have highly active thinking parts will obsess, contemplate, and talk about the pros and cons of a situation without ever making a decision. Thinking keeps everything in the head, making it harder to know what feels right. For example, one may think: "There are so many houses I've looked at that I like. I can't figure out which one is the right home to purchase."

When one tries to decide without self-connection, there's often *a sense of loss* associated with whatever is chosen. For instance: "If I buy the house on Green Street, then I can't have that beautiful bungalow on Laramie Avenue." These clients frequently ruminate, worry, get stuck, and can be misdiagnosed with OCD. However, if you begin to listen, you'll realize that it's their thinking parts working overtime to protect them from feeling the emptiness, loneliness, and loss that's buried deep down inside.

Consider the following dialogue between me and my client Brian:

"Brian, I've noticed that you're spending a lot of time in this session trying to figure out how many courses you should teach this semester," I said. "Do you have a sense as to what feels right for you?"

"There are too many good options," Brian responded. "I guess that's a good problem to have, but I know that the ones I choose will affect my supervisor's view of me. I just can't make a decision."

"Which would make you the happiest?"

"I have no idea."

"Let's take a moment and see if we can approach this from a slightly different angle," I suggested. "What if you stop trying to figure out which courses to pick? What shows up inside?"

"Nothing, nothing at all."

"What's happening in your body?" I asked.

"I feel a knot in my stomach."

"Can you focus on that knot for a moment?"

"It's like a pit in the bottom of my stomach. It makes me so nervous."

"See if you can stay with it for a few seconds longer."

"I don't know what it is, but at least I'm feeling something for a change," Brian commented after a few silent moments.

"Let the part that's trying to decide and the sensations in the pit of your stomach know that we're going to move slowly here. There's no hurry at all; we're just going to be with them right now in this moment."

"That feels really good inside. You're staying with me and helping me sort this all out. I didn't get much of that as a kid," noted Brian.

Here, the client begins to see that the importance is not so much about the correct decision but more about someone being there with him to help him sort out his feelings, thoughts, and bodily sensations. He had to do this all by himself growing up, and his thinking part did its absolute best to try and sort things out for him.

Another thing I've noticed about clients who suffer from histories of neglect is *my tendency to overshare.* Several of my clients present as if they haven't a clue how to navigate their life, saying things like: "What do you mean? I don't know how to do that. I've never thought about that before. What do you think I should do?" Neglect leaves clients at a loss, as if they don't have any life experiences from which to draw, which may be true. Yet I've noticed that I have this penchant to share my personal experiences with these clients, and they tend to find it helpful in some way. It gives them something *real* to connect with. I might remark: "Here's what happened to me when my oldest started dating" or "When I get frustrated with my husband, I sometimes feel this way." Of course, we need to be careful about boundaries and what we're sharing from our personal lives. Is it coming from the Self or from a caretaking part? But for these clients, I find that sharing some of my experiences helps them connect in a way that their neglected parts have not experienced before. I always ask myself: "What is the purpose of sharing? Whom does it benefit?"

Neglect is a silent injury associated with profound, long-lasting effects that can take years to fully resolve.

RESILIENCE

We know from the ACE study that there are significant developmental and mental health differences between children who have minimal trauma and secure early attachment experiences compared to kids with severe trauma and less secure early relational experiences (van der Kolk, 2014). There are, however, certain individuals who seem to experience horrific trauma and can somehow overcome it. They have something extra within them: the internal desire, drive, and capacity to overcome difficult circumstances, even when the odds are stacked against them. Who are these people? What do they possess? And how did they get this way? Is it nature (temperament) or nurture (environment) at work? Bessel van der Kolk believes that *resilience*, or the capacity to bounce back from adversity, connects to the level of security established with the primary caregiver during the first two years of life (van der Kolk, 2014).

I agree with van der Kolk, to some degree. I'm not totally sure what has contributed to my capacity to overcome my trauma as well as I have. It's true that I have a significant history of trauma, but I've also had an internal fighter in me most of my life. I remember as a child saying to myself: "I'm not going to let this get to me. I'll never stop fighting. They're not going to win." During my psychiatry residency years, I remember reading the book *Soul Murder* by Leonard Shengold and immediately thinking: "No, that didn't happen to me." I had this voice deep down inside of me that was never destroyed or silenced. Is this the Self? Is this due to secure attachment? Is this resilience? How did I get it? Why do some of us seem to have more of this than others? I've benefitted greatly from therapy and suspect I will forever continue my healing journey. I have an internal drive to improve and better myself. Whatever that quality is, I've seen it in some of my most severely traumatized clients. I'm grateful that I possess some of it too. It has saved my life.

POLARIZATIONS IN TRAUMA

Polarizations are extremely common with trauma. On the surface, it looks as though they perpetuate untenable circumstances, create immobility with no obvious solution, and result in confusion and frustration for all parts involved. Clients may say: "I like this guy, but he frequently pushes me too far sexually" or "I get how being suicidal protects me, but it causes so many problems with my wife and kids." When different parts hold seemingly different views, it's not only challenging for them, but it also perpetuates tension and distress in our clients. When therapists approach the dilemma from fix-it or problem-solving parts of themselves, it can create frustration and feelings of inadequacy within the therapist too.

Polarizations rooted in relational betrayal are typically more powerful and extreme and create an all-or-nothing scenario in clients. This is how many trauma survivors frequently get diagnosed with borderline personality disorder, often due to unsolvable polarities within volatile relationships. You may hear clients reveal things like: "I love my dad, but he becomes a total monster when he drinks" or "I can't live without my boyfriend, but I hate when he's violent and disrespectful." Even though each side of a polarization appears to hold important and opposing views, they often (but not always) protect the same wound. For example, a comment such as "I can't live without my boyfriend, but I hate when he's violent and disrespectful" most likely reveals two parts that are protecting a young attachment wound that wanted love and connection from an abusive caregiver.

Ponder the case of my client Charlie. He was able to truly listen to his numbing part. He learned how vital this part was to his system and how it protected him from the terror he experienced at the hands of his psychotic mother during childhood. Charlie was also able to separate and hear from the part of him that wanted to be more present and active in his life. Here's a conversation we engaged in during a session:

"These parts have been at war with each other for years," Charlie said. "I get it in a different way now—they both have legitimate arguments."

"Charlie, can you check and see if they're both protecting the same little boy inside who was hurt by your mom?" I asked.

After a few moments, Charlie responded: "Believe it or not, they aren't protecting the same kid in there. The numbing part is definitely related to my mother. And the other part, the one that wants a fuller life, is connected to a part of me that was always on the outside looking in. You know—the last one picked for sports, never being invited to any of the school birthday parties, the last one asked to dance at prom."

"I hear that, Charlie. What would you like to say to these parts right now, if anything?"

"I want to let them know they don't have to fight anymore, that my heart is open to both of them, and I have enough love to go around."

"Can they take that in from you, Charlie, and are they willing to give us some space to be able to help who they have been guarding for so long?"

"What I can tell you is this: There's so much relief inside right now, and this is the first time a solution even seems remotely possible for each of them. This has been such a huge battle inside of me for so many years," Charlie replied, his body now in a more relaxed and peaceful pose.

Self-energy is a tangible solution to many, if not all, polarizations. When it's available in both the therapist and the client, and they're open to hear both sides of the story, it usually becomes clear to all involved that each side has a valid point. It's also clear that everyone benefits, both inside and out, when they listen to suggestions from the Self.

Any time Self-energy is present, even if another part of the system is polarized with it, I have my client send that healing energy directly to the target part before we address the opposing part's concern. To demonstrate, consider the following discourse between me and a client named Linda:

> "I'm feeling mixed right now," Linda said. "I truly appreciate the angry part and how it's trying to help me. I'm also aware that there's a part of me who's afraid of the anger and its destructive potential."
>
> "Linda, can you send those appreciative feelings toward the angry part first? Then see if it's able to take that in [sending Self to the target part]. Now let's get to know the part of you that's afraid of the anger and see what it wants to share with us [addressing the part that's polarized with the Self]. I'm sure it has a good reason for feeling this way," I said.

(Remember: Polarizations that involve Self-energy will resolve more quickly when the target part, in this case the anger, can take in the healing power of the Self.)

> "The fearful part seems more relaxed now," Linda said. "She saw how kind and respectful I was with the anger. She really likes that."

When there's a polarization between two different parts, having the Self listen and validate both views can help resolve the dilemma. When the Self is part of the polarization, have the Self send positive energy toward the target part first. That way,

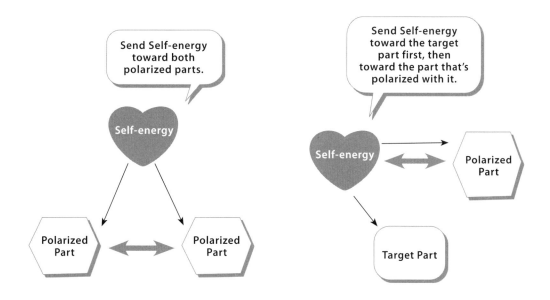

the part that's polarized with the Self can witness and take in the benefits of the Self firsthand, which typically settles the conflict more swiftly (as shown in the graphic on page 131).

Polarizations tend to be an overcorrection to an overwhelming experience, but they are unfortunately the norm for clients who have been relationally violated. Conflicts, opposing views, untenable situations without a solution, and being stuck are commonplace. Protector polarizations are a brilliant and effective way to keep well-intentioned therapists confused and guessing while ultimately keeping the vulnerable, wounded feelings at a safe distance.

CHAPTER 19

Trauma, Feelings, and Loss

A Nontraditional Approach to Parts

Some clients don't take to parts language easily. Some have a hard time going inside, while others have parts that don't work in the typical IFS fashion. I find this common, but not exclusive, with clients who have highly intellectualized systems. These parts need to be in control. They need to talk extensively and for long periods of time before they'll relax and give permission. With these clients, I tend to employ IFS therapy without ever using any of the typical language. I don't say "part." I never ask anyone to "step back." And I don't ask my clients to "go inside." Instead, I engage with the client in a traditional talk therapy approach because that's what their system seems to require.

However, I always follow the IFS model in the back of my mind. As I talk with a client, I notice protective parts show up, and I listen for the wounds they protect. I engage parts in conversations without them explicitly knowing that's what we're doing, and I seek permission to access wounds. We're able to release painful experiences without formally going through the steps of the unburdening process. The therapy moves forward but at a much slower pace. Protectors eventually give permission, and wounds reveal themselves and release what they're carrying. All of this occurs without ever looking or sounding like typical IFS therapy.

For proof as to how this can work, take a closer look at my client Debra—an intelligent, high-powered business executive who runs several companies. Debra likes to be in control, and parts of her need to be in control. Here's a snippet of an exchange with Debra during a session:

"Can we pick up where we left off last week? I've been thinking about what you said about my relationship with my daughter," Debra said. "I agree with you that I'm afraid to talk to her."

"What do you think is your biggest concern?" I asked.

"When it comes right down to it, I think I'm afraid to be vulnerable with her. I guess I know I am. If I'm going to be honest with her about the affair, I worry that she'll judge me. I also worry that her drinking problems are related to her watching me and her mom fighting all the time."

"What if you were able to go and visit her and listen to her perspective first, before telling her about yours?"

"I think that's a great idea," replied Debra.

"Do you have any idea where your difficulty with vulnerability came from?" I asked her.

"My best guess is that it's connected to my relationship with my mom and how she constantly criticized me whenever I did something below her high standards. But I'm not sure."

"That makes sense to me, Debra. See what your gut is telling you," I suggested.

"It feels right," Debra said.

Debra was ultimately able to talk to her daughter, to listen to her perspective, and to be honest with her about the affair once she was able to identify her own fears and connect with her painful experiences related to the relationship with her mom. But notice that this exchange never used words such as "parts," "stepping back," or "How do you feel toward that part?" Yet you can see that I was still talking to her about her parts, learning about their concerns, helping them to unblend, and revealing the exile underneath her protectors.

TRAUMATIC AFFECT AND EMOTION

It's important to be able to distinguish between feelings and traumatic affect. They're not the same and are often inaccurately equated. *Traumatic affect is not an emotion but an intense expression of an overwhelming symptom or reaction that is typically held in protective parts.* It's an exaggerated response to devastating or violating circumstances. Yelling, cutting, and being suicidal, hypervigilant, dissociative, or reactive are physiological reactions to overwhelming events, not feelings. Trauma also includes *feelings*, which can be held within protective parts (e.g., feeling angry, afraid, or remorseful) or exiles (e.g., feeling alone, unlovable, or worthless).

Both the reactions to trauma and the feelings associated with it can be intense. IFS has a way of directly dealing with these overwhelming responses. IFS therapists address protectors and exiles alike, asking them through direct access to *not overwhelm the system* so the Self can safely be present and compassionate with whatever they're holding and wanting to share.

Throughout my personal therapy, I frequently confused traumatic affect with feelings. It was not until my trauma symptoms diminished and my protectors began to trust my Self more and stopped taking the lead that I was able to be with my feelings (my exiles' emotions) more authentically. My feelings were more manageable when they were in sync with my Self. They began to make sense and feel aligned with my truth for the first time in my life. Traumatic affect is associated with reactivity, intensity, and impulsivity, and the energy it carries can be big but different from a feeling. Differentiating between traumatic affect (mostly protective parts) and emotion (mostly exiles' feelings) helps pave the way toward releasing the painful experience once and for all.

LOSS, BETRAYAL, SAYING NO, AND LETTING GO

While loss is a normal part of life, it is difficult to manage. When we lose a family member, friend, or loved one, we experience an enormous amount of pain and grief. Complex trauma survivors, on the other hand, will often experience *any amount of loss in traumatic proportions*. When a loss occurs for them, not only are they experiencing emotions related to their current-day experience, but it also triggers repeated relational losses from their past. *It's a double trauma for them.* The result is additive, and the loss is experienced in catastrophic proportions. Survivors live through the loss of the present while reliving, yet again, losses from the past.

I feel like I've developed a subspecialty as a grief counselor because of my work with relational trauma survivors. For these clients, small losses can feel overwhelming, and more significant losses can cause them to completely decompensate. This awareness will hopefully help you remain in Self-energy when counseling a client who appears to be "overreacting" to what may appear to be minimal but which is experienced as profound when it's confounded by the past.

Betrayal also triggers a similar seemingly exaggerated response. When intimacy is violated, it's certainly hard to recover from. But with complex trauma clients, a betrayal often feels cataclysmic. I have rarely seen a trauma survivor recover, for example, from a partner's infidelity. It's not impossible, but it's extremely difficult due to the activation of young, wounded parts inside that still hold unbearable pain around the repeated relational rupture they endured years ago at the hands of their abuser.

Loss is particularly hard when it's associated with repeated relational disconnection. Take the case of an adolescent client named Abby, for instance. When Abby's mom is triggered, she loses her safe and reliable mother and is forced to interact with a reactive or out-of-control part of her. When her dad is drunk, Abby loses the father she loves and tries her best to please and placate his drunk counterpart.

These repeated relational losses create protective parts within our clients that have the exhausting job of doing whatever they can to prevent and protect against yet another painful loss. Unfortunately, this attempt by protective parts to seek out relationships that prevent reoccurring losses in childhood often results in clients choosing partners who will likely leave or abandon them.

I've become more aware over the years that many of the decisions I've made in my life have been rooted in loss prevention. For example, I have had *a hard time saying no to things*. When someone would make a request, I previously tended to say: "Sure, I'll teach next month," "That would be fun—I'd love to be a part of that project," or "Okay, son, you can buy a new bike." When I went inside myself to examine why it was so hard for me to say no, I heard: "If we say no, we'll lose out on something fun and exciting," and "If we say no, they won't like us anymore." Both of these parts of me would often take over and say yes to prevent me from feeling a loss of any kind, including the loss of a fun experience or the loss of a connection. I'm happy to say that I've been able to unburden these wounds, and my life is in much better balance now—thanks to IFS.

Are you aware of parts of you that react and respond so that you won't have to experience the feeling of loss?

When we're united with our truth in feeling, we experience a sense of well-being and know that we're on the right path. However, being aligned can also involve some loss. You might think: "If I say yes to this, it means I'll have to say no to that." This is generally well tolerated, especially when it's connected to a decision that feels right and is connected to the Self. If we say no to something that's affiliated with what we *think* we should do, or what others want us to do, or what our protective parts want in the service of protecting a wound, we're more externally driven, and the feelings of loss are generally more intense and harder to tolerate.

Saying no also requires *tolerating feelings in other people* too, which can be just as challenging. You might find yourself thinking: "If I say no to going out to dinner with friends, or if I say no to taking on a new client, I'll have to tolerate them potentially being disappointed with me." Worrying that others will respond in an angry or disappointed way is not an easy thing for trauma survivors, as it potentially activates the energy of their protective parts. Making decisions requires the capacity to tolerate missed opportunities, feelings of loss that arise, and uncomfortable feelings in others. When we connect to our feelings from the Self, as opposed to from parts, decisions are easier to make, and the feelings that emerge are easier to tolerate.

Struggling with loss can also result in *hoarding behavior*. I've worked with several clients over the years who've struggled with attachment wounds connected to an abusive or neglectful parent. They've developed protective parts that feel the need to hold on to everything and anything in a desperate attempt to avoid the pain associated with the loss of their primary attachment relationship growing up.

One client of mine traveled from one apartment to the next, always taking with her 15 boxes of stuffed animals that her father gave her when she was younger. I've joked with other hoarding clients about my making a home visit someday, awaiting the mortified look on their face because they fear that I am serious and would actually see what they've accumulated over the years. Sadly, many never feel able to move out of their homes because of the enormous amount of time and energy it would take to pack up all their belongings. I try to help these clients connect with what they need to hold on to and what they can let go of. This is related to the items they've accrued, as well as their memories of people who have both loved and hurt them so much.

The biggest loss of all for complex trauma survivors is *the loss of their Self*. Miguel's wounded part said it perfectly: "As if it wasn't bad enough that my brother sexually abused me, that my mother was constantly depressed in bed, and that my dad was a raging maniac every time he got angry, through it all, I lost my Self over and over and over again." Repairing the injury created between parts and the Self as a result of trauma is one of the true gifts of IFS.

The following is a summary of parts commonly associated with loss.

- **Parts affected by betrayal and infidelity**
- **Parts that lose when someone is triggered or abusive**
- **Parts that don't say no in fear of loss**
- **Parts that agree or say yes to prevent loss**
- **Parts that hoard objects in lieu of people**
- **Parts that lose the Self as a result of trauma**

CHAPTER 20

Therapist Parts

From my perspective, the main focuses of IFS Level 1 training are to help therapists: (1) learn to be proficient at the model, (2) get to know their parts better, and (3) be more aware of and less susceptible to being triggered when counseling clients. When the therapist's parts get triggered by the client's needy, desperate, anxious, or avoidant parts, it can be challenging to actively listen to clients, respond appropriately to their needs, set limits, and maintain healthy boundaries. When we respond from a part of us, it has a particular energy associated with it that clients subconsciously perceive and react to from one of their parts. For example, when one of our controlling parts attempts to set a boundary, the clients can respond in several ways—from getting angry, pushing back, or disconnecting to appearing needy or desperate for contact and connection.

When therapists react from a caretaking part, they give too much of themselves in an attempt to rescue and help. This response might initially feel wonderful to some parts of our clients, but other parts of them become alarmed and feel like the therapist has crossed the therapeutic line, causing them to fight back or shut down in an attempt at self-preservation. When activated, *therapist parts often give too much, withhold too much, offer advice, or act rigidly*, which can trigger a range of protective parts in our clients.

I once had a client named Joe, for whom I was serving as a backup therapist. Joe emailed me with concerns about Sienna, his primary therapist, writing:

"Frank, can you please help with Sienna? She's in the hospital right now for something related to her colon. Sienna keeps calling me at night before she goes to bed to make sure that I'm safe and not drinking or cutting. Can you please help me out here and tell her to stop calling me? She's a therapist—she should be taking care of herself, not worrying about me."

I realized immediately that Sienna's caretaker part had taken over, and I could only imagine what Joe's parts must have said or done to elicit that overprotective response in her. I knew that Joe could certainly get into some serious self-destructive patterns, so I refrained from criticizing or blaming Sienna. Instead, I had compassion for Sienna and her parts that felt overly concerned for him. I also felt bad for Joe's parts that were experiencing Sienna as intrusive. Today, I no longer think in terms of countertransference, as I was taught in my residency training; I think about therapist parts in reaction to and in relationship with clients' parts.

Setting boundaries from the Self instead of parts feels quite different. We're calmer and clearer and speak from a different internal place, and our clients respond to our energy from a different place within themselves. They can feel the difference between our centered presence versus our driven agenda. When we're in Self-energy, they may think: "Thank goodness someone is in charge here."

I recently had to tell a client named Mary: "I'll do my best to be there for you whenever you need me. But as you know, I have two kids and travel a lot. There could be times when I won't be available for you, unfortunately. But if it's urgent and you haven't heard back from me, by all means, please try me again." I said these words from the heart, from my Self. Mary's response was positive: "Thanks, Dr. Anderson. That means a lot to me. I appreciate it." As a result, I rarely get calls from my clients during off-hours. They know I genuinely will be there for them when I can, and I know that they sincerely don't want to be intrusive in my life. This is what I call establishing *Self-to-Self boundaries*.

For clients who struggle with attachment trauma, the therapist's Self is a vital presence, especially during the early stages of treatment. Often, these clients do not yet have a lot of access to their Self-energy, and they rely heavily on the therapist's calming effect. I tend to call this the *Self of the therapeutic system*, or the collective Self-energy of the therapist and client. In some instances, the ratio could be wildly disproportionate— say, 98 percent therapist's Self and 2 percent client's Self—especially in the beginning of treatment. However, as clients begin to listen to their parts and learn about the parts' jobs and fears, more Self-energy becomes available to them. Eventually, the ratio becomes a 50-50 share of the collective Self-energy between therapist and client. Soon, the client's Self can lead their internal system more independently.

When the client's Self takes the lead—a process Dick Schwartz calls *passing the baton*—it can be particularly challenging for some of the client's young attachment parts. Remember that these young parts have developed a strong trusting relationship with the therapist's Self, and they're often terrified of losing that connection when the client's Self begins to take the lead more often. From the young parts' perspective, the client's Self was the one who abandoned them at the time of the trauma, not the therapist's Self, so they are often not thrilled about this transition.

THERAPIST SELF-CARE: BETWEEN-SESSION MEDITATION

I now make it a general practice to eat a few almonds, visit the washroom, and engage in a brief meditation between sessions. I take a moment to go inside, scan what's there, and identify any feelings or energy I've picked up or carried from my previous client. I then acknowledge the presence of these unwanted elements and ask them to leave my system. I often gain important insights about my clients during these quiet moments of introspection following a session, and I will jot down these observations in the client's chart.

Once I've cleared the energy from my previous client, I'll internally send them love and compassion and check to see if any of my parts became activated. If so, I listen carefully to these parts, validate their feelings, energetically reestablish my boundaries, and ask these parts to relax and allow Self-energy to return within me. Once I sense this shift, I open up space for my next client, internally sending them love and compassion before I externally summon them from the waiting room so that we can begin our session.

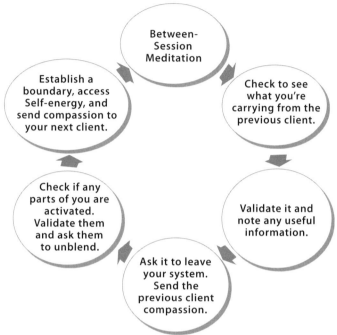

ATTACHMENT AND THE THERAPIST

Clients with attachment trauma have a range of parts, and among them are exiled parts that can develop strong attachments to their therapist. With the natural ebb and flow of the therapeutic process, these parts of your clients can react in not-so-obvious ways to your comings and goings.

During my residency, where most of my supervisors were psychoanalysts, we spent an inordinate amount of time focusing on the transference issues that got stirred in our clients when we took time off or went on vacations. It felt much more theoretical than actual to me back then. Our clinical rotations lasted from three to six months at the most, and I assume it was possible, although unlikely, that my clients got that attached to me in such a short timeframe. I felt like the supervisors were unduly emphasizing my importance in my clients' lives. Looking back, I was probably right.

Fast-forward to now, with me being in full-time private practice for several years. I acknowledge that many of my clients with attachment trauma definitely seem to be affected by my comings and goings—only not in the way my supervisors said it would unfold. I find that my clients often react in disguised ways that can take me time to identify. One client named Calvin would casually bring up his desire to try EMDR with another practitioner while I was away. Being an open-minded therapist, I explored with Calvin the pros and cons of this decision. It took us both time to figure out that his desire to experiment with EMDR was connected to my increased travel schedule. Complicating matters was the fact that Calvin was also a therapist. His exiles were, for the most part, well-hidden. When we would explore a possible connection to his interest in EMDR and my upcoming departure, Calvin would experience tension in the chest, tightness in the shoulders, or stomach pain. It took us over a year to connect the activation in his body with his exiled part, who held grief, despair, and occasional suicidal ideation due to repeatedly being dropped off at boarding school as a child.

Another client, Wanda, had parts that were insistent about how useless, unsupportive, and unavailable her Self was. It took us a while to associate this feeling with my periodic leaves from practice. After several years of therapy, she was eventually able to connect with and speak for the parts of her that felt abandoned by me—parts that, in her words, were "constantly being thrown to the wolves." We quickly learned that they were referring to Wanda's Self as the wolves.

Again, making these connections around loss can be challenging, especially with a client who has parts that are young, ill-defined, and largely unknown to their system. It's not as obvious and direct as my supervisors had explained it would be during my residency. But the importance we carry for the young parts of our clients who have suffered from attachment trauma is certainly worth paying attention to.

Being Relational but Not Taking It Personally

Being connected and relationally available to your client while maintaining appropriate distance, keeping proper perspective, and remaining in Self-energy can be challenging, especially when you're dealing with desperate or dysregulated parts of the client. I've found it difficult at times to not get taken over by certain parts of me that developed in my childhood. When I was younger, my parents would frequently tell me what I was feeling and what I should be thinking. I remember my response was more to challenge than comply, saying things like "No, that's not what I'm feeling" or "Don't tell me what I'm thinking." I had a stubborn part that I later learned was fighting for self-preservation. How grateful I am for that part!

However, today when my clients tell me what I'm thinking or feeling, my younger part still tends to show up. I have always admired Dick Schwartz and his ability to not internalize what clients project onto him. Triggered parts of clients will often cast their beliefs about their abuser onto their therapist, particularly when they subordinate or sense an unbalanced power differential within the therapeutic relationship.

When clients bring these perspectives and distortions into the office, *I have found it important to validate the part's perception first* (as it's coming from an important place in their past) while trying my best to not take it personally and remain relationally curious, available, and connected. This is easier said than done. Remember what Louis Cozolino said: that most of the input to the cortex comes from internal processes, and we scan for examples that prove our preexisting beliefs, primarily driven by fear to avoid danger (Cozolino, 2010). I find this insight extremely helpful. I try to remember that a client's perception of me in those moments is often rooted in their past experience and has very little, if anything, to do with me.

I don't always do such a great job with this struggle because my associated wound is not fully healed yet. I am still sometimes affected by the relational aspects of a connection to a client. Case in point: Consider my experience with a client named Peter. Peter's standing appointment time had changed from noon to 11 a.m., and the first week this change went into effect, he was late. It was approaching 11:30 a.m., so I sent Peter an email reminding him of the time change. I didn't hear from him until the following day. He called and left me a phone message in a spiteful tone, saying: "I'm so upset that I missed my appointment, I guess I'll see you next week." The following week, Peter showed up 15 minutes late for his appointment and was furious at me. Here's an exchange we had:

> "I've been waiting for your car to show up in the parking lot," Peter said. "I didn't think you were here. Why didn't you call me and tell me you were here?"

> "I'm sorry, Peter. My car's in the shop right now. I drove a loaner vehicle today. I've been here the whole time waiting for you," I replied.

> Peter began to escalate. "You know, you could have called last week instead of emailing me, and you should have called me today when you noticed I was late," he said angrily.

If the parts from my childhood weren't activated, I could have validated his experience and said something like:

> "Peter, I see that you're angry with me for not reaching out to you by phone last week, and you wish I would have called to see where you were this week. You seem pretty upset. I totally get it. I'm interested in hearing more about your experience."

Then, hopefully, after his angry part felt seen and heard, we could have explored what was behind this protector's response. Instead, I replied this way:

> "Wow, Peter. It's really hard for me to be attacked like this. I did reach out to you last week, in the way I do with all of my clients, and I am sorry that you didn't know that I was driving a different car this week. But it doesn't feel great to be attacked like this. Hopefully, we can turn this into an opportunity to help you learn how to work through difficult moments in relationships. I know this is something you've struggled with in the past."

I observed Peter tear up for a brief moment, and then his angry tone and face quickly returned. I suddenly realized I had lost an opportunity to genuinely connect with Peter and his vulnerable parts by sharing my experience with him before I was able to listen to and validate his parts.

I don't think we do our clients any favors by allowing them to *be in their parts* and barrage us with their hurtful attacks. On the other hand, challenging their projected beliefs can further alienate and enrage their extreme parts. The beauty of IFS is that it doesn't do either of the above but incorporates both. The Self can tolerate intense feelings and distorted views, avoid taking them personally, and name what's happening in a non-shaming way—all while still maintaining the open curiosity to access the true origins of the trigger.

WHAT ARE WE OFFERING?

As a consummate caretaker, I have grown to value and appreciate what I consider to be IFS's unique perspective on healing, which can be summarized in the answer to an important question: What are we offering our clients? Are we offering a healthy corrective relational experience that is therapeutic, or are we offering to help them heal their wounds by connecting to their Self?

IFS offers the latter. We help our clients access their Self-energy, and we support their Self as the corrective, healing experience for their parts that carry past pain. In my experience, as echoed by one of my clients, the Self can offer what no one else can: the ability to repair the breach that formed during the original assault, as well as a unique bonding experience powered by true acceptance and love. In IFS, therapists can offer their Self as an adjunct to healing, and when they do, ideally it comes from a place of compassion, not empathy. Remember that compassion is a desire to help that includes care, distance, and perspective (Self-energy), while empathy is an activated part of the therapist that resonates with the client's painful experience.

Some therapeutic modalities hold a different view. They posit that the therapeutic relationship is corrective and healing for clients. I'm not saying they are wrong and IFS is right. I'm simply pointing out a difference between IFS and some other models of therapy. *In IFS, the internal Self-to-part connection is the primary healing relationship, and the therapeutic relationship is adjunctive or secondary to that.* In other words, the internal relationship is reparative, and the external relationship is supportive of that process.

Consider the case of my client Emma. During a particularly poignant moment in one of her therapy sessions, Emma's little girl part took over and said to me:

> "Will you be patient with me? Will you not leave me?"

> In the gentlest way possible, I said: "Of course, I'll be patient with you, but I can't promise you that I won't leave you." Emma looked up at me and started to cry.

> "I'm totally committed to helping you," I continued, "but what if I were to tell you that Emma can be there for you in a way that no one else can or ever was? Would you be interested in that?"

"Don't worry. I'm fine on my own," Emma said in her self-reliant caretaker voice. "I always have been, and I always will be. Daddy left me, the maid left me, and mommy left me too. Everyone leaves, and I learned how to take care of myself."

"What if I were to show you there's an Emma in there you haven't met yet who is capable of being there for you and loving you in the way you deserve? Are you interested in that?"

"Perhaps," responded Emma's part.

Here, the offer is clear: Emma's Self can be the corrective healing agent that her wounded parts need and want. Often, younger parts aren't yet fully connected to the Self I'm offering them. That's because the chasm between the Self and the part bearing the betrayal has not been fully repaired yet, much like we discussed earlier between the target part and the current-day Self. *We also introduce the wounded part to the Self of today*, the Self that is capable of listening to the client, being there for her, loving her, and not abandoning her as before. The Self of today is older, wiser, and more capable than it was back then. This is a result of age, development, capacity, and time. Again, Self-energy is the primary offer in IFS; the therapeutic relationship, although extremely important, takes a back seat and serves an adjunctive or supportive role.

CHAPTER 21

Common Comorbidities

Real Mind-Body Medicine: The Intersection Between Parts and Biology

In IFS, we often identify areas of the body linked to parts. One of the first questions we ask our clients when we're trying to identify the target part is: "Where is the part located in or around your body?" As I've described earlier, I believe that parts live in the mind and utilize the brain and body to express themselves. This intersection between parts and the body is important, especially when it comes to medical illnesses and physical symptoms.

How much are your client's repetitive headaches the result of a part trying to get their attention, and to what degree are they related to cluster migraines, to which the client is genetically predisposed? *It turns out that parts are incredibly helpful at sorting out this question*; more often than not, it's a percentage of both. For example, 60 percent of the migraine may be connected to parts while 40 percent is biologically rooted.

I have had a long history of what is called "cough variant asthma." This means that whenever I get a cold, I'm susceptible to experiencing an asthmatic reaction in my lungs that causes a chronic cough that can last for months. This requires me to take several medications, including inhalers, antihistamines, and steroids. There are some seasons when I've gotten sick and it doesn't trigger my asthma, and other times when I experience repeated asthmatic reactions.

I have done a lot of work in therapy with my parts around my reactive airway disease, and I've learned a great deal from them about my propensity for this reaction in my body. They've told me my asthma is genetic to some degree. (I generally hear this information from what sounds like a collective voice in my head.) My father has an overactive immune system that manifests as rheumatoid arthritis; for me, it presents as a hyperimmune response in my lungs. I've also learned that parts will sometimes show up in my throat to remind me that I'm out of alignment in some important way and not speaking my truth.

I have conflict-avoidant parts too and have a hard time speaking up when there's something difficult I need to say to someone. It often takes me by surprise when I get this information from my parts because I wasn't conscious of it. But when I hear them speak up to me, it feels right.

For example, I knew in my gut it was time for me to leave the Foundation for Self Leadership (FSL). I had spent five wonderful years connecting with the IFS community, working with wonderful board members, learning about how to run a not-for-profit organization, and supporting the expansion of IFS. It was hard for parts of me to acknowledge that it was time to move on, and it was even harder to speak this truth out loud to my friends and colleagues. At the time, I was traveling a lot and caught a cold, which triggered a severe asthmatic reaction. It wasn't until I began taking prescribed steroids, which cause numerous unwanted side effects, that I started asking what, if anything, was going on from the parts' perspective. I heard: "You know in your heart it's time to leave, but you're afraid of disappointing everyone."

After hearing this, I was able to connect with and heal the younger part of me that was terrified to speak up to my father as a child. Doing this piece of internal work made it much easier for me to voice my intentions and tell those I loved and cared about that it was, in fact, time for me to leave. My parts watched as I told the FSL board about my departure, and they were surprised at how everyone reacted. No one yelled or raised dissent. Everyone was happy for me and supportive of my decision. And my cough, yet again, resolved.

Parts and biological conditions have a strong relationship with each other. As Dick Schwartz often says, *parts can push the biological button*. My parts were telling me: "We caused the asthma attack to get your attention because you are not speaking up." And the reverse is also true. *Biological conditions can often affect parts*, causing them to say: "This isn't us—we have nothing to do with the asthma attack. It's the winter, the heat is on, the air is dry, and you're allergic to dust." At other times, it's a combination of both parts and biology, where they share a percentage of the responsibility. All we have to do is ask; parts are usually willing to help sort things out.

I recently worked with a client named Antonio who was recovering from a heart attack. Here is a sample of the dialogue we shared:

> "Antonio, I wonder if you're open to listening to your parts about your recent heart attack," I said.
>
> "What do you mean? Do you think I caused it or something?"
>
> "No, I'm not saying that at all. I think that there's a strong mind-body connection, and perhaps your parts might be able to help us understand if there's any connection between what they're carrying and your physical symptoms."
>
> "I guess so," Antonio said.
>
> "Just ask if any of your parts knows anything about your heart attack."
>
> "This is fascinating," Antonio said with his eyes closed. "I would have never guessed this in a million years. What I'm hearing is that there is a connection to my job: 'You've worked so hard for so many years to become a partner at that firm. You gave them everything—long days and many nights and weekends away from the family. You busted your butt for them, and now this new management team is treating you like crap.' What they are telling me is true. I feel like I have no power anymore. My parts are saying that they're brokenhearted."

"Wow, that makes so much sense to me, Antonio," I responded. "Let them know that we're hearing this."

"Oh, you bet I will. I had no idea that this was going on inside," Antonio said, who then paused a moment. "They say it's 50-50. They say I'm not eating clean and not nearly exercising enough—that half of this is medical and the other 50 percent is about their heartbreak."

"Let them know you're really getting all of this, Antonio."

"You know what? This is an echo of my childhood. I worked so hard as a kid too, trying to get my parents to see me and love me, and it never worked. They were always too busy with one thing or another. They never seemed to have the time to care about me. Now I feel like it's happening all over again at work."

"Let your parts know that there's a way we can help them with the feelings they're carrying about your childhood and that it most likely will help you better manage the current problems at work. Are they interested in that?"

"Yes, definitely. They're so happy we asked them about all of this. They said I wasn't caring about them, in the same way that my employer and parents didn't care about me."

"All of these layers and connections make a lot of sense, Antonio. What do you want to say to them about that?"

"I'm not going to repeat this pattern. The buck stops here," he said with conviction.

When we hear from parts that the anxiety, difficulty sleeping, and worrying is related to them, we learn how the symptoms help to protect, and we gain access to healing the underlying wound. But when parts say the anxiety, difficulty sleeping, and worry is not theirs, we must consider whether it's biologically based and perhaps associated with symptoms of depression, for example. *Typically, when symptoms are rooted in a biological condition, they affect the whole system, and all parts are equally distressed by them.* We then ask parts if they would like help with the anxiety, sleep trouble, and worry. If they all agree, we explore medical solutions to address the problem.

I believe that most medical problems and comorbid psychiatric conditions from which people suffer are partially due to their overall system being out of alignment in important ways. Holding on to unexpressed feelings, engaging in activities that aren't aligned with our truth, or ignoring our inner voice can manifest as either mental or physical symptoms. Parts can use our bodies to communicate with us that something inside isn't quite right.

Gabor Maté speaks of this phenomenon in stating: "Mind and the body are inseparable, and illness and health cannot be understood in isolation from the life histories, social context, and emotional patterns of human beings" (Maté, 2011, p. xi). Maté made the bold statement that several of his patients who suffer from a wide range of illnesses associated with chronic inflammation have never learned to say no in important areas of their life. He is also careful not to blame people for their illnesses: "There is no responsibility without awareness." His goal is to promote learning and healing, not blame and shame, which he believes is overabundant in our culture. Maté advocates for self-awareness and self-connection in the service of disease prevention. He's a fan of IFS, and I'm a fan of his perspective on the connection between trauma, emotions, and medical illness.

IFS Treatment for PTSD and Comorbid Depression: A Pilot Study

I was fortunate enough to be involved in a research study supported by the FSL that examined 13 subjects with PTSD who had histories of multiple forms of childhood trauma, including sexual abuse (65 percent), psychological maltreatment (65 percent), and physical abuse (59 percent; Hodgdon et al., 2017). The subjects participated in sixteen weeks of IFS therapy, and after treatment, 12 of the 13 subjects (92 percent) no longer qualified for a PTSD diagnosis according to the Clinician-Administered PTSD Scale (CAPS; Weathers et al., 2018).

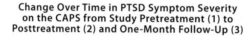

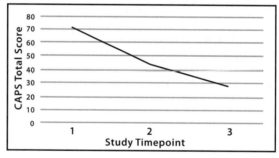

Change Over Time in PTSD Symptom Severity on the CAPS from Study Pretreatment (1) to Posttreatment (2) and One-Month Follow-Up (3)

Statistically significant decreases in depression were also noted, as measured by the Beck Depression Inventory (BDI; Beck et al., 1961). Decreases were seen for affect dysregulation, dissociation, disrupted self-perception, interpersonal relationships, and systems of meaning as well.

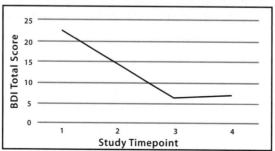

Change Over Time in Depression Symptom Severity on the BDI from Study Pretreatment (1) to Mid-Treatment (2), Posttreatment (3) and One-Month Follow-Up (4)

PSYCHOSIS, BIPOLAR DISORDER, AND TRAUMA

Years ago, I attended a residency program that primarily served clients who were homeless and had no health insurance. Many of them suffered from major mental illnesses and severe substance use. Because the majority of our supervisors were psychoanalysts, we learned to explore the function or underlying meaning of a client's psychotic symptoms while simultaneously treating the chemical abnormalities occurring in their brain. I discovered that if you feel alone or isolated, being paranoid can make sense. Believing the FBI or some covert operation is spying on you around the clock, or being convinced that Jesus talks to you regularly, can make you feel special and important if you're feeling inadequate, lonely, or insecure.

I learned long ago—as IFS teaches today—to view the positive intention of all symptoms, even with psychotic symptoms or parts that hold psychotic beliefs. I have never met a client with bipolar disorder who didn't describe what they were fleeing from after they'd recovered from their most current manic episode. The majority of the time, these clients had some underlying trauma history or traumatic loss that they were escaping during their manic periods.

In IFS, we also look for the positive intention of any psychotic thought process. And we try to sort out which portion of the symptom is affiliated with some form of protection and which portion is biologically based that could benefit from medical intervention.

People with severe complex trauma, PTSD, and dissociative disorders can *appear* psychotic, especially when they're dysregulated. The neurobiological abnormalities resulting from their trauma make it difficult to adequately process thoughts and feelings when they're triggered. They can present as confused, distressed, and dysregulated in a way that mimics a thought disorder. *One of the differences between psychosis and trauma dysregulation is that the latter recovers once the client is no longer triggered, but psychosis persists well beyond the present activation.* Parts also require different interventions to help them unblend.

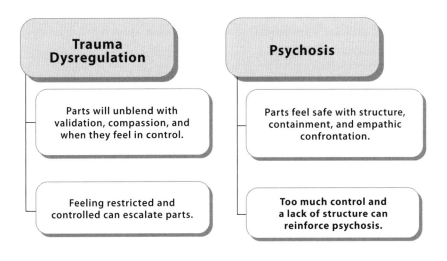

Clients who suffer from trauma have rarely had their perception of reality validated, and their control has often been violated or taken away. Therefore, traumatized parts need to have their experiences validated and to feel a sense of control so they can unblend. However, with psychosis the opposite is true: excess validation, too much control, and reinforcement of their distorted beliefs and feelings can perpetuate or reinforce psychotic thinking. These thought-disordered parts need limits, structure, and a sense of safety, which can be accomplished when someone gently names what is actually happening in reality because their internal experience is often frightening, chaotic, distorted, and internally overwhelming.

Clients with severe attachment trauma or those who are labeled with disorganized attachment can have young exiled parts that develop distorted or psychotic attachments. These young parts often hold confusing experiences or carry mixed burdens from their past in connection with their primary caregivers. For example, this client may say: "My father is loving during the day and a violent monster at night" or "My mother is physically intrusive, but I still love her and need her for survival." I've had two such clients in my career, both of whom I treated for several years. In each example, the clients formed psychotic attachments to me slowly over time, and it was hard for me to recognize it until it was profoundly entrenched.

I made the mistake of not confronting the distorted thinking early on in the treatment. In retrospect, I was too gentle and supportive of their view and unknowingly reinforced their beliefs. These young parts don't have the cognitive capacity to differentiate reality from their perception of reality, and there was often no one there to help them do so. In addition, these parts will often feel blamed or shamed when the reality *is* pointed out to them. The therapist's Self can conduct delicate conversations with these clients—conversations that name and hold the balance between reality and the exiled part's experience. If both are not addressed or closely monitored, psychotic attachments can be fostered.

Working with parts that hold psychotic beliefs generally takes longer and is more challenging. *This is due to the delicate balance required when naming reality without shaming the part and validating the experience without fostering distortion.* It also takes time to decipher the language of psychosis. However, when healing occurs, clients feel tremendous relief and are enormously grateful because they no longer have to carry nonreality in the service of survival.

CHAPTER 22

Medications and Trauma

PARTS AND MEDICATION

Medications play a significant role in treating trauma. Most clients experience at least one comorbidity or a part overtaken by symptoms like depression, panic, obsessive worrying, attentional difficulty, or sleep problems. Therapists need to work closely with clients to determine if a medication trial is warranted. For a more detailed exploration of the relationship between medications and IFS, refer to the chapter I wrote, titled "Who's Taking What? Connecting Neuroscience, Psychopharmacology, and Internal Family Systems for Trauma," which appears in *Internal Family Systems Therapy: New Dimensions* (Anderson, 2013).

When therapy feels stuck and progress has been halted, ponder comorbid biological conditions and potential medication trials. A medication can serve as an effective *unblending agent* when clients are too stuck in their parts and have difficulty achieving separation. Medications tend to work more effectively when *all parts agree to take them*, and there are usually fewer side effects when all parts give consent.

Parts have been known to *interfere with medications* too, and they can "create" side effects when not adequately consulted. Parts know how to use the internet and scour for facts that suit their interests. They're even capable of blocking medications from working. I've heard parts tell me: "I'm the one that blocked the Trazodone from making us sleep" and "I stopped the Zoloft from working."

I once had a client named William who had a history involving early attachment trauma that included verbal abuse and neglect. He struggled with anxiety and dissociation, and his parts had a hard time separating from him so that he could get to know them better. William spent most of our time together being overwhelmed by anxiety and feeling numb, detached, and dissociated. Trying direct access proved helpful at times, but William's physical symptoms dominated the sessions, preventing us from making progress.

I asked William to check inside and see if his parts were interested in taking any medications to help with his anxiety or dissociation. But it quickly became clear that taking medicine for anxiety wasn't a possibility due to his dissociation. All of William's parts (except the dissociative one, which would not relinquish control), wanted help for the anxiety and were willing to try pharmaceuticals. Over time, the dissociative part hesitantly agreed, and William started on a low dose of Celexa.

After a few weeks, his anxiety lessened, and he was able to benefit from the space the medication provided for his system. It opened the door for him and me to engage the dissociative part more actively in a discussion. We learned that this part was the last responder and felt the need to jump in when things got bad enough inside. The dissociative part became active when William was 11 years old, when he started witnessing his mother suffer beatings by his father. We both appreciated the necessity of the protection that the dissociative part provided, and the part appreciated being known and respected for its role. It also appreciated not being forced into taking a medication. The dissociative part was eventually willing to soften further and would accept a low dose of Abilify, taken as needed when things got too intense for it. As you can see, working with parts around medication decisions often reveals clinically significant information.

Manager or preventive parts tend to *love* medications and are usually willing to take them, as opposed to extreme or reactive parts that need to be in control and typically refuse prescribed medications or will only take them as needed. I encourage all therapists to keep their own parts and personal views in check around medications and to stay closely connected with their clients' wishes throughout the prescribing process. Prescribers generally have minimal time to spend with clients, so it's important for therapists, who generally have a more trusting relationship with clients, to take the time and help them sort out their fears and to accept the risks of allowing a foreign substance into their bodies.

Wounded parts have also been known to request help from a medication, especially when they're struggling to manage the intensity of overwhelming traumatic affect. For clients with trauma histories, it's important to achieve harmony among all parts and to resolve opposing views before you refer them to a prescriber. Their success will greatly improve if all parts agree.

PSYCHEDELIC-ASSISTED PSYCHOTHERAPY

Psychedelic-assisted psychotherapy is a rapidly expanding treatment option for trauma survivors. Under the right circumstances, it can provide additional help and support for some who have struggled to heal from their overwhelming life experiences. The Multidisciplinary Association for Psychedelic Studies (MAPS) is an organization spearheading much of the research associated with the psychedelic-assisted psychotherapy movement. They have supported research connected to 3,4-Methylenedioxymethamphetamine (MDMA), the main psychedelic drug currently used in PTSD-assisted psychotherapy. MDMA is also being studied for the treatment of anxiety associated with life-threatening illnesses and for social anxiety in adults with autism spectrum disorder.

MAPS also advocates clinical trials of medical marijuana for the treatment of PTSD among war veterans and ayahuasca-assisted treatment for PTSD and drug addiction. It has examined LSD-assisted psychotherapy for anxiety and has sponsored studies for ibogaine therapy for drug addiction. In addition, psilocybin, also known as magic mushrooms, is being studied for the treatment of major depression, alcohol dependence, OCD, and cancer, among other things.

Ketamine, the only FDA-approved psychedelic to date, is currently prescribed for treatment-resistant depression and is being studied for alcohol and heroin addiction. It is also being used in conjunction with psychotherapy to treat a variety of mental health–related issues. I am trained in ketamine assisted psychotherapy (KAP) and look forward to exploring the various ways it can help trauma survivors get beyond their extreme protective parts and heal their underlying wounds.

It's encouraging to see this group of medicines being used to treat a wide range of mental health–related issues, and I suspect their use will further expand as the research evolves. MDMA, the most well-studied psychedelic to date for treating PTSD, seems to be beneficial in helping clients increase self-compassion (Self-energy, in IFS terms). It has been shown to reduce defenses and fear of emotional injury (i.e., protective parts) and make unpleasant memories less disturbing while enhancing communication and capacity for introspection (Multidisciplinary Association for Psychedelic Studies, 2020). I support the use of MDMA for clients with extreme trauma histories who have a difficult time accessing Self-energy on their own.

However, not all psychedelic drugs should be treated equally because they each work on different receptors and neurotransmitter systems, and they have a different mechanism of action. For example, we may discover that MDMA is more beneficial for clients who have difficulty accessing Self-energy because it increases self-compassion. We may see that ketamine, which decreases excitability, is more helpful for protective parts that have trouble relaxing or stepping back.

As research and clinical experiences continue to expand, we'll get a better sense as to which medications and dosages are effective for which clinical circumstance. It's important to remember that these medications must be used with caution because they do have abuse potential and are harmful when used in excess or without proper supervision. The preliminary results look quite promising, and I truly believe that this group of medicines will provide innovative approaches and new exciting treatment options for a variety of medical and mental health–related issues. I encourage you to visit www.MAPS.org for further information.

Healing

CHAPTER 23

Healing Emotional Wounds

AN ATTEMPT AT RIGHTING THE WRONG

The parts that carry emotional hurt and physical pain from the past are often locked away deep within the psyche. It can sometimes take months or years to locate and gain access to these exiled parts, especially when you're dealing with more extreme forms of trauma and neglect. However, these parts tend to run the show, take a toll, and have a huge influence over a client's daily life. Many complex trauma systems spend much of their time and energy in the form of a *redo*, or an attempt to fix the problems of the past with someone in the present day. In other words, they end up in a continual state of redemption. For example, you may hear clients say things like: "My boyfriend will love me in a way that my father never did," "My friend Emily will be there for me in a way my mother never was," and "My kids will feel loved by me in a way that I never felt loved by my parents."

Exiled parts are in a perpetual state of wanting rescue. For many of them, fixing the past in the present day seems like the best available option. Unfortunately, however, this repeatedly fails and causes protective parts to once again jump in, which inevitably reinforces the original trauma. It's painful for me to see so many of my chronic trauma survivors stuck in a perpetual attempt at emancipation, which inevitably results in their picking a slightly upgraded version of their perpetrator and re-creating a version of their history.

In IFS, we offer a different kind of redo for our clients: a redo that involves their Self as the true corrective experience, not someone in their present day who shouldn't and can't help them right the wrong of long ago. The latter approach tends to have a very high failure rate. *The Self is the ultimate in corrective experiences for parts.*

Case in point: Consider an exchange I had with Darnell, a client with a strong and prominent caretaking part that, he learned, commandeered a large portion of his life and played a crucial part in his decision-making.

> "When I ask inside, I hear that 20 percent of what I do for other people is related to wanting them to like me. I've known that about myself for a while now. But what I'm learning for the first time is that I also take care of people so they won't feel the same pain that my little boy did when he

was abused, and that is a big percentage of this part. I'm hearing inside that this is about 80 percent," Darnell said. "This has been a perpetual problem for me in my life in so many ways. I started a nonprofit organization, and this part of me has given away ridiculous amounts of money throughout my life. For Chrissake, I just paid for my daughter's best friend to go to private school next year. Do you think this part is also related to the trouble I've had with setting boundaries with people?"

"I don't know, Darnell," I replied. "Let's ask the part and see what it says."

"I know you keep harping on this boundary thing. But I'm now realizing that the reason it's so hard for me to say no to anyone is also related to this part trying its best to prevent people from feeling rejected like my little boy did back then," Darnell said. "I can see now how this has been an eternal problem for me that will never get fixed. Apparently, I keep trying to help the boy by taking care of everyone else. Thank goodness I'm finally getting it now. If we weren't doing this work, I think I would be bankrupt."

"Let the caretaking part know that we can release the little boy's pain, and it will no longer feel the need to take care of everything and everyone else all the time."

"He's nodding and smiling from ear to ear right now," Darnell said.

KEEPING IT HIDDEN

It's common and often uncomfortable for clients to exude the energy of a wounded, suffering victim. But it's important to help clients appreciate that this energy is an attempt by the exile to be seen, known, saved, and rescued without being consciously recognized or directly identified.

Therapists should work with the client on holding this *under-the-radar feeling* so the client knows it, acknowledges it, and keeps it alive without exposing too much of it in a way that activates protective parts. Therapists can gently name the energy of the exile and slowly bring it to conscious awareness even before protectors have given permission to formally access the wound. Saying too much too soon will be met with denial and pushback. But when the client displays enough Self-energy, naming what is below the surface can be helpful and illuminating to clients. I refer to this as *speaking beyond protectors* or implicit direct access with exiles. For example, consider talking to a client as such:

"Jody, I sense that there are some tender parts in there that are hurting. And I want them to know that we'll eventually come for them and help them let go of their sorrow," I said. "However, we need to do this in a way that's safe and respectful of all parts. When the timing is right, I promise we will come for them."

"When you just said that, I noticed that I instantly felt calmer," Jody said.

The awareness by the Self of the exiles' energy can help protectors and exiles alike feel comforted and hopeful.

It's also important to be mindful that with relational trauma, healing the exile may not automatically solve the problem. It's common for there to be multiple exiles that need to be cumulatively healed over time, and it's important to be aware that protective parts often carry their own pain and burdens that secondarily need attention.

THE ORDER OF HEALING

By trusting the wisdom of the Self, we let the client's system decide what order is appropriate when it comes to healing wounds. My clients will often want to make a list of their traumas to track their progress, which is fine with me. In fact, it can be quite useful, especially when their protective parts try to distract us by heading in other directions. Have your parts relax when it comes to what they think the order of healing should be. I have a general belief that clients move from the "outside in" when it comes to healing. In other words, they focus first on less intense trauma then move toward more painful and impactful trauma.

I was recently surprised when Kirsten, one of my clients, wanted to make a list of her traumas and proceeded to do so in what I would say was the typical order: less to more intense. As she started focusing on her relationship with her boss, she stopped herself mid-sentence and said:

> "We need to talk about my mother. She's really at the root of all of my insecurities in life. If we focus on her, all the rest will naturally fall into place," Kirsten said.

> "Sounds like a good plan," I noted.

I love this model and love trusting my clients' internal processes and healing wisdom. I would have never come up with that plan for Kirsten, and it was clearly the right way to go for her.

THE ISSUE OF RESPONSIBILITY AND ADDRESSING DISTORTED BELIEFS

It's common for parts of the system to show up that feel responsible for what happened to them, especially with trauma that occurs in childhood. Remember: If the one who was in power doesn't take responsibility for what they've done, it's natural for the recipient to have parts that believe it's their fault. Clients often say: "It must have been my fault" or "If I did or said something different, then maybe it wouldn't have happened." When parts like this show up (and they frequently do), *I ideally have my client's Self challenge the distorted belief over my attempting to do it because it's often much more impactful*, as evidenced in the following exchange I had with a client:

> "José, what do you want to say to that little boy who thinks it was his fault that his father hated him so much?"

Here, the Self is the great normalizer of the distortion, and when the connection between the part and the Self is securely in place, the part will likely be able to take it in.

"I want to tell him he was just a boy, and it was dad's responsibility to not get drunk and not yell at him all the time. It wasn't his fault at all," José said.

"Was he able to take that in?" I asked.

"Yes. His body softens as I say it to him."

A client of mine named Dawn had a horrific history of childhood trauma, which included a group of men sexually abusing her on multiple occasions. A particularly poignant session unfolded concerning this issue of responsibility when Self-energy was present. Dawn was able to listen to the little girl who lived her whole life feeling bad and believing that everything was her fault. Here is a sample of our conversation:

"Oh, my goodness—it feels like I'm finally getting it. The little girl inside of me is telling me that taking responsibility for everything was a way for her to not accept what those men did to her. She's saying, 'If I take responsibility for everything bad that happened to me, then I don't have to see what really did happen,'" Dawn said, now beginning to cry.

"It's a huge deal for her to let go of blaming herself and see and accept what really happened," Dawn continued. "She's also telling me that all the OCD stuff—the counting, the repeating, the lining everything up—is an extension of trying to take control and responsibility for every aspect of her life. It was another way in which she didn't have to see the reality. She's so exhausted from all of this. My heart is breaking for her right now."

"Great work, Dawn. I'm really glad you're fully getting this. Just stay with the little girl and give her what she needs right now," I said, feeling a full heart and high emotions because I was simultaneously connecting to the ways I tried to control and deny the reality of my own trauma.

Distorted beliefs held by parts within a traumatic system are often hidden, normalized, and out of conscious awareness. It's important for therapists to listen closely for these distortions, as they usually come up nonchalantly in therapeutic conversations. I was struck when a spiritual healer I often see called out some beliefs that were indoctrinated into my system. "Frank, who says you can't have a successful career and good relationships with your kids? What part of you thinks it needs to hold onto the pain of your childhood?" I was honestly shocked and taken aback when these beliefs were named. They felt like "truths" or "just the way it was." I was blended with them, and they felt normal to me. Having these beliefs brought to my attention allowed me to connect with the parts that held them and enabled me to unburden the exile underneath that felt it wasn't allowed and didn't deserve to feel good.

DIFFERENT TYPES OF WOUNDS

In the section on attachment trauma, we talked about two different types of wounds that can develop in children when growing up. One is the *collective wound*, in which a main exile holds many different traumas over several years (e.g., "young Timmy" holding trauma due to the loss of his mother, the bullying he experienced at school because of his attention-deficit/hyperactivity disorder, and the fatal car accident he witnessed as a teen). The other wound type is what I call a *developmental wound*, where a similar trauma is experienced repetitively over several different developmental stages (e.g., a client's 5-year-old, 8-year-old, and 12-year-old parts all hold aspects of dad being bipolar, intermittently out of control, and verbally abusive).

There is also what I call *parental wound pairing*, which occurs when children grow up in a dysfunctional family and develop a significant wound related to each parent (assuming it's a two-parent household). Here, one wound is primary and the other is secondary, typically resulting from a part of one parent that is activated, hyperaroused, and in relationship with the other parent's part that is withdrawn and hypoaroused (e.g., when one parent is verbally abusive and the other is passive, distant, and overly tolerant, or when one parent is sexually abusive and the other is dissociated and emotionally vacant). These parent pairings are unfortunately common, and children typically will develop two different wounds based on their responses to each of their parents' parts. These are the clients who are typically diagnosed with borderline personality disorder or disorganized attachment in my experience.

Clients can also develop a set of parental pairing wounds that result from two activated parental parts or two blunted parental parts. These circumstances can be quite toxic for children and create deeply embedded wounds. When both parents are constantly fighting or are often emotionally vacant and unavailable, there's no counterbalanced reality for children to experience. All they know is one side of an extreme, which can produce profound and intractable wounds internally.

Richard, a past client of mine, once described the difficulty he encountered setting limits with his oldest daughter. A portion of our dialogue follows:

"I know it sounds crazy. I know I should be able to do this, but I just can't say no to her," Richard said.

"Let's see if you can go inside and ask if any parts know anything about this," I suggested.

"Well, I see the little boy—the one who was the little husband to my mother. There's still so much pain. He doesn't want my daughter Sarah to ever feel anything close to what he's feeling. If I disappoint her, she might feel sad or hurt like he did."

"That makes sense, Richard."

"I also remember constantly apologizing for everything I did when I was younger, even when I did nothing wrong. I remember thinking that if I was really good, maybe my mom wouldn't do those things to me."

"That makes sense too, Richard," I said.

"But when I kept apologizing, my dad would always explode at me, especially when he was drinking. 'Stop being such a goddamn baby,' he would say over and over again."

"I'm sorry you went through that as a child, Richard. It sounds horrible. Can you see if the little boy is holding both of these experiences—what your mom did to him and how your dad would explode?"

After a few moments, Richard said: "No. There are two separate kids in there. One is connected to my mom, and the other is related to my dad."

"Okay, let them know we're hearing them and that we're going to help both of them get out of there for good," I said. "Which one makes sense to focus on first?"

"Being touched and left alone is first, and being yelled at is second," Richard said without hesitation.

"Alright then, that's how we'll proceed."

Most clients don't come into treatment to heal their childhood wounds. Tom comes in because he's drinking too much and it's destroying his marriage. Juanita is underperforming at work and recently got fired from yet another job. I call these current-day traumas or present-day wounds, knowing that most of them are additionally connected to a core wound or past trauma. I refer to this trauma combination as a *double trauma*, one from the present connected to one from the past. For example, drinking too much affects Tom's marriage, but it's also protecting him from feeling unloved by his mother growing up. Or disconnecting and underperforming at work costs Juanita her job, but it also helps her avoid feeling invisible in her family as a child.

Most, if not all, current-day traumas have some link or connection to an earlier event or experience that's buried and was never fully dealt with. The present-day or secondary trauma compounds and adds to the pain of the primary or core wound. They both eventually need to be healed for protectors to let go of their job and for the system to feel fully free from the pain it shares or has in common. Many individuals experienced this during the COVID-19 pandemic, when the global trauma of quarantine, isolation, job loss, sickness, and death additionally triggered or reactivated difficult or painful experiences from their past.

Unfortunately, it's also possible for some trauma survivors to have *several wounds related to multiple traumas*. More often than not, but not exclusively, these clients will get a diagnosis of DID.

The following is a summary of the various types of wounds.

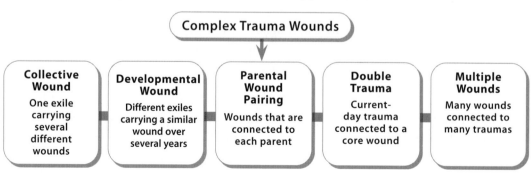

THE STEPS OF HEALING: THE UNBURDENING PROCESS

I always recommend that therapists who are interested in incorporating the unburdening process into their clinical practice complete Level 1 training through the IFS Institute (www.IFS-Institute.com). If you have not been fully trained, I suggest working with protective parts and—if and when an exile shows up—that you don't proceed with an unburdening but continue with what you're formally trained in or feel most comfortable with when dealing with vulnerability. If you are proceeding with IFS, once you and your client's Self have successfully encountered, connected with, and received permission from all protective parts associated with the wound in question, it's time for the client's present-day Self to meet the exile of the past. Here's an example, using a past session with a client named Ashley:

> "How do you feel toward the girl inside who was abused by her older brother?" I asked.

> "I'm feeling a lot of love for her right now," Ashley said.

> "Let her know that, and see if she can take that in from you."

> "She says she doesn't want sympathy."

Just as is the case with protective parts, exiles are often in connection with the Self of the past just before it left the overwhelming experience. We need to make sure they are fully updated and in connection with the Self of today before proceeding with the steps of unburdening.

> "Ashley, see if she's willing to see that you're not that little girl anymore; see if she can see your essence now."

> "Yes, she's seeing me now," Ashley noted. "She says I'm really old."

> "Great. Give her some time to get to know and trust you."

Now we're ready for *witnessing*—the first step of the unburdening process, which allows the exiled part to share with the Self all that it's carrying about the event. We make sure that the part shares not only the story but also the emotions, beliefs, and physical sensations associated with the trauma. Here is where *the exile often requires both empathy and compassion from the Self.* It needs the Self to be with it as a compassionate witness, and it often requires the Self to feel some of what it carries through empathic resonance. I often check in with the client's Self periodically to make sure the amount of sharing isn't overwhelming, as it can appear quite intense at times.

> "Ashley, are you okay with what the little girl is sharing with you right now?" I asked.

> "Yes," she replied. "I'm getting for the first time the terror she experienced that day, and I want to be with her."

"Great, let her know that."

Once witnessing is complete, the part no longer feels like the only holder of the information around the trauma. For the first time, the part begins to feel that it no longer needs to carry the experience for the system; the Self can do that job. Be mindful that witnessing—or as Braca Ettinger, a French artist and psychoanalyst, refers to it: "wit(h)nessing" (Ettinger, 2001)—can take several sessions or even months to fully complete.

Do-over and *retrieval* come next. Here, we instruct the Self to enter the scene where the exile is and to give it what it needed and wanted but never got. First, the do-over allows for the corrective experience we covered earlier, where the Self is the corrective object for the part, not the therapist. This is often emotional for the therapist to witness and the client's part to experience, as the Self is giving the part the love and attention it so desperately wanted and deserved. Next is the retrieval, where the Self takes the part out of the past and brings it somewhere safe in the present day. Here, I said to Ashley:

"Ashley, let that little girl know she will never have to go back there again."

I want her to get the message that this will be permanent. I let the part choose where it wants to go as long as it's in the present day. I also want to make sure that the Self is with the little girl directly as opposed to a Self-like part showing up to help out.

"Ashley, are you seeing yourself with the little girl [a Self-like part], or are you there with her directly [the Self]?"

"I'm with her. She wants to go to my daughter's bedroom," Ashley replied.

"Great, let me know when she's there."

After the part is safe in the present day, we invite it to *unload* all of its thoughts, feelings, and physical sensations out of its body. This typically happens through a release of energy that's transferred to some form of nature, although this is not a requirement.

"She wants to first burn it in a fire and let it float up into the sky," Ashley said of her part.

"Good. Let her do that now, Ashley, and make sure that she releases all of it," I said, mindful that if the part does not fully unload all that it's carrying, the burden can return.

"She feels lighter and seems so much happier now."

"Terrific. Let her take in any qualities that she might need as she moves forward," I said, urging Ashley to take the step we call *the invitation*.

"She wants to take in confidence and have the ability to speak up."

"Good. Let her do that now."

The last step is *integration*.

"Ashley, let's bring in all the parts that have been protecting her and let them see her now."

"They're shocked," Ashley said. "They can't believe how happy, free, and relaxed she looks."

"Wonderful. Let them know they can let go of the job of protecting her now and that she's safe with you now. Also, let them know that we'll check in with them next week to see how they're doing and if they would like to unload anything they're still carrying."

This is often the case in trauma—that protective parts also need to unload what they were forced to hold in the service of protection.

The following diagram represents the six steps involved in the unburdening process.

Witnessing
- Have the part share with the Self all that it's holding.

Do-over
- Have the Self go into the scene and give the part a corrective experience.

Retrieval
- Take the part out of the past and bring it somewhere safe in the present.

Unload
- Have the part release the thoughts, feelings, and physical sensations.

Invitation
- Allow the part to take in qualities it needs as it moves forward.

Integration
- Bring protectors back to see the unburdened part and suggest the release of their roles.

DIFFERENT TYPES OF HEALING

One of the main things that makes healing from relational trauma so difficult is that there's often very little *access* to Self-energy in clients who have repeatedly been violated, betrayed, or attacked. This is a major frustration for therapists and clients alike. These clients have complicated, entrenched systems and experience difficulty convincing protective parts to relax and allow Self-energy to emerge. The container theory states that when the number and intensity of protective parts take up most of the space within "the container," there is less available space for the Self. I believe a combination of access and willingness to heal from a traumatized system allows the gift of Self-energy to emerge. It becomes an issue of exposing vulnerability for systems that have experienced the horrific.

Next, we'll explore what I believe are the different types of unburdening that occur when you're working with complex trauma survivors.

DIRECT ACCESS UNBURDENING

When protective parts hold more energy within a system than the Self does, a *direct access unburdening* is often necessary. Direct access unburdening is when the steps of the unburdening process are primarily performed by the therapist's Self in connection with the client's exile. This can feel extreme at times because the client is often fully blended in the wounded part's experience and reliving the event to some degree. The therapist's Self does the witnessing and gives the part what it needed, wanted, and never got. (This step is particularly tricky, especially if the part wants to be held and the therapist does not routinely incorporate touch into their practice.) I generally discourage therapists from having physical contact with clients who have experienced abuse, as it can activate younger attachment desires and trigger the reexperience of abusive touch. You'll have to make your best clinical judgment if and when this occurs with each particular client.

The therapist then encourages the part to leave the past, to come into the present, to release what it's holding, and to enter new qualities, just as we do in a traditional unburdening. What's different is that the therapist is the Self here. This unburdening typically doesn't have the same impact on the client's system as does an unburdening that includes the client's Self. However, a direct access unburdening is often a necessary preliminary step in the overall healing process when a client doesn't have enough access to their Self. It ultimately helps to bring more Self-energy into the client's system.

This type of unburdening is rare and is usually needed during the early stages of treatment with clients who have DID. It is also beneficial with extreme protective parts that are unwilling to separate and that need to unburden what they're carrying before they are willing to give permission to access the wound. *I don't recommend trying this unless you feel very confident and comfortable with the IFS unburdening process*, as it can be overwhelming for even the most seasoned clinician.

One of my clients was very sweet when she explained the difference between direct access unburdening and the healing sessions we did when her Self was more present. She told me:

> "Please don't take this the wrong way, Dr. Anderson. I appreciated it when you were the one helping my little girl, but it feels so different when I'm there too."

Anya, one of my clients, had an extremely anxious part that jumped in every time a feeling emerged. When I performed direct access with that protective part, we learned that it not only blocked all feelings, but it also carried them, including emotions strongly connected to her numerous childhood traumas. Remember, parts can hold a complicated range of feelings, beliefs, and behaviors. Anya's anxious part liked talking to me and enjoyed feeling heard in a way that it hadn't before. It was ready to give access to her 7-year-old girl who was sexually violated by her older brother.

"I'm not ready to include Anya in this yet," Anya's anxious part said. "I hold the feelings about missing our brother so much, and the 7-year-old holds what my brother did to us. Anya is acting too calm right now. I don't trust her."

"What if it were possible for you to be connected to both Anya and to the little girl at the same time?" I suggested to the anxious part.

"No. If I connect with Anya, I'll lose the connection to the little girl. Anya still loves her brother too much."

"I have a suggestion: What if the little girl shares her feeling with you and me first? Then, together, we can share your feelings and the little girl's feelings with Anya. Would that be alright with you?" I asked the anxious part.

"Yes, that's the only way it will work," responded Anya's anxious part.

"Okay, I trust that you know what's best."

"And I trust you," the anxious part said. "Thanks for taking the time to listen to my side of things."

"You're very welcome," I said.

Remember: Loving and appreciating the wisdom of parts and the natural order of healing is always the best way to move forward.

Anya and I then proceeded with a direct access unburdening. Her 7-year-old shared images of the event, while the anxious part shared feelings of grief and loss for her brother. It was incredibly moving to be the witness of the joining of these two parts. We later learned that Anya's Self was watching this unfold from a distance.

"Finally, after all these years, I now know why I'm so uncomfortable with anyone touching me, why I won't let anyone walk behind me, and why I cry like a baby at sad movies," Anya remarked.

Clearly, our work had an important impact on Anya, her parts, and her therapist.

Some healings will begin as a direct access unburdening and evolve into a more traditional unburdening at the end. For example, witnessing will primarily be done by the therapist's Self, and the client's Self will later emerge to complete the remainder of the steps.

RELATIONAL HEALING

When there's very little, if any, Self-energy available or accessible within your client's system, direct access unburdening is often helpful, if not required. As the Self becomes more available over time, there's a middle stage where the client's Self is present but perhaps not present enough for the system to feel safe enough to attempt an unburdening without extra or outside help. This is what I call *relational unburdening*, where the client's Self is present and the therapist's Self or another person is needed to help complete the unburdening process. Relational unburdening is common with exiles that hold attachment trauma, with exiles that have significant neglect histories, or with clients who carry a diagnosis of DID. *Remember, it's important to let the client's Self direct what the therapist's Self should do to help during the healing process.*

To illustrate this point, consider the following case involving a client named Luke, who had a relationally challenging adulthood. Before he entered therapy, he had been single for most of his life and desperately wanted to be in a relationship someday. We spent the first two years of therapy getting to know a range of his protectors, especially the harsh critic (internally and externally directed) and the highly intellectual part—which were both reluctant to step back and would constantly talk *about* what happened in Luke's life, always void of emotion. Eventually, we got permission from these pervasive parts to access some of Luke's exiles. Much to his surprise, we discovered a range of exiles that all carried similar experiences (i.e., a developmental wound).

> "Now I understand why I never really knew who I was growing up. There are so many different parts in here," Luke said.

> "Let's just be open and try to listen to what they want to share with us. Let's leave it up to them, if that's okay with you," I recommended.

> "They seem to start around the age of 6 and go all the way up through my late teenage years—around 17 or 18," Luke said. "They want to talk together in some ways but also have some specific things to share too. Is that okay?"

> "It's totally fine with me."

> "They all seem so alone. They've been hiding out for years. The 17-year-old was the one who needed to step up to the plate and function in the world. The 12-year-old always felt so awkward in his body. And the 8-year-old never fit in socially at school. None of them could stand up for themselves, and no one ever felt good enough. The 6-year-old feels like crying right now, and so do I," Luke said.

> "It is sad, Luke."

> "One of the problems was that when they did cry, my mom would yell at them and say, 'What's wrong with you? Stop crying!'"

"Luke, let them all know that we want to hear what they've been holding for you."

"They feel like we're beginning to get it. They're holding so much sadness and feeling alone."

"Luke, let them know that it's totally fine with us that they're sad. They have a lot to be sad about. Are you able to be with them right now in the way they need you to be?"

"No, not really, without your help. It's too much. They like and trust you a lot more than they trust me right now."

"That's alright. Let them know that you and I together can help them hold the sadness. I'll be here every step of the way," I assured Luke. "Let them share with us what they need to share."

"It's all about the feelings right now."

"Luke, see if they can share the feelings a little bit at a time until they feel like we have all of it," I suggested, trying to help them manage the overwhelm.

"Okay," Luke said. A silent moment passed before he added, "I think we're good."

"Ask them just to make sure."

"Yes, it's alright now," Luke said.

"Can you go into the scene and give them what they needed and wanted back then, and then bring them somewhere safe into the present?" I asked.

"Yes, they feel like they've gotten what they needed from us, and now they're ready to leave."

"Good. Do they want to go as a group, or does it feel better for them to go one at a time?" I asked.

"Definitely together."

"Perfect, let them know they can unload all the feelings, thoughts, and beliefs they've been carrying in any way that works for them," I suggested.

"It's floating up into the sky and dissolving into thin air," Luke described. "It's so sad, but it also feels so peaceful."

"Wonderful. When they're ready, have them take in what they need to be able to move forward in life."

"Love and belonging. And the assurance that they matter," Luke said, with a calm and knowing look on his face. "Thank you so much, Frank. This was amazing."

"I know. I feel honored to be sharing this with you right now, Luke."

"This is the kind of closeness I've been missing all of my life."

"Let them know you can have this in your life now, with someone who you love and want to share your life with," I said with a pause. "Can we now check in with the critic and the intellectual part?"

"Oh, they're both so happy. They've been watching this whole time. They are blown away. I feel so much love for all of these parts right now. It makes total sense to me now—they've been the watchdogs for years."

"Keep sending them love and appreciation, Luke."

"They love that. And they deserve it too," a teary-eyed Luke said.

My presence was very important to Luke's parts, but I did let his system direct what needed to happen and in what order. I needed to be present for emotional and relational support without controlling the process or taking over.

Relational unburdening can also happen when working with a couple. Here, one member of the relationship is in the role of the observer while lending their Self-energy to the partner who is engaged in healing their wound (Herbine-Blank, Kerpelman, & Sweezy, 2016). This allows an unburdening to occur in the context of a loving connection, which can be quite powerful for both people in different ways. We know that Self-energy is a powerful healing force; collectively, it can add a level of safety and comfort to parts that carry and need to let go of their pain. We witness the collective power of Self-energy time and time again during live demonstrations that occur during IFS training.

CUMULATIVE UNBURDENING

Complex trauma survivors who engage in one-on-one therapy typically don't have access to the same collective Self-energy that is present in training demonstrations, so the healing process usually progresses at a slower pace. It takes a long time to get to know all the players in the system and for them to trust you enough to consider stepping back. Once a small percentage of the client's Self is available to connect with the wounded part, witnessing can happen a little bit during each session until the process is fully completed—which, in some cases, occurs over several months. With each session, a bit more witnessing takes place. This process is typically long and drawn out: Week after week, session after session, more of the story unfolds until the exile feels the Self and/or the therapist fully comprehends it. Witnessing this way, slowly over several weeks, is a great way for exiles to avoid overwhelming the system.

Once this is complete, the remaining steps of the unburdening process typically unfold over the next few sessions (i.e., the retrieval, do-over, unloading, invitation, and integration). I call this way of healing *cumulative unburdening*. This incremental healing transpires over several weeks with an extended witnessing phase. I also find that cumulative unburdenings don't necessarily follow the traditional steps in the typical order. In one session, there may be some witnessing and a bit of retrieval that occurs. In another follow-up session, there may be more witnessing and some unloading. Again, it happens gradually over multiple sessions.

Unburdening relational shame rooted in abandonment and neglect also takes much longer than a traditional unburdening. Protectors are fierce and reluctant to step back and give permission. Self-energy is often not readily available or minimally present, and if you move too quickly, parts push back, and healing is less impactful for the system. This type of healing requires an enormous amount of patience and Self-energy from the therapist and can take weeks to months before it's complete due to the entrenched nature of the trauma.

For proof, ponder the case of Blake, a 46-year-old gay client who originally entered treatment because he was having difficulty in his relationship with his husband, Troy. It didn't take us long to learn about the origins of his intimacy problems. Blake had a strong internal storyteller who knew all the details of his abusive father, who left when Blake was 7 years old, and his alcoholic and critical mother who was left behind to raise four boys on her own. It took us over two years to get permission from all of Blake's parts to connect directly with the little boy inside. They were inflexible, often unwilling to soften, and reluctant to give us access, fearing the intensity of the boy's feelings. But eventually, Blake was able to connect with his Self, and his parts let him meet the boy, who ranged from 4 to 16 years old. Blake referred to this collective wound as "little B," a child who would be banished if he ever asked for anything—a boy who was constantly criticized by his "bitch of a mother," according to Blake.

"All you had to do was think about yourself," Blake said, tearing up. "Little B constantly felt like a nonentity. He had horrible self-esteem."

"Blake, are you hearing this directly from him, or is another part sharing this information?" I asked.

"It's coming from him. It's like he's transmitting his feelings directly to me. I'm really with him right now."

"Great. Let him know you're getting it, Blake."

"I remember when I got my first job in high school. I was afraid to even put my name on the badges we were required to wear. I didn't want anyone to know who I was or what a failure I had become. Sorry—I'll get back to little B," Blake said, admitting that he was alternating between different ages. "Little B and I are feeling so sad right now."

"It's totally fine. Let it unfold naturally," I instructed.

"He never thought anyone would ever stay with him."

"It sounds like he carries some shame, Blake."

"Oh my God, yes—an enormous amount."

"Let him know we'll keep coming back to him so he can share all that he's holding around your dad leaving and your mom being so nasty. Let him know we're here to help him."

"He says we have to do this a little at a time; that's all he can handle. He's saying there's a lot there, and it's going to take some time."

"Let him know that's fine. We're in no hurry here. He can take as long as he needs," I replied.

"He really likes that."

After about three months of slow witnessing, little B was ready to come into the present and unload what he was carrying. Blake's whole demeanor changed: He became calmer, more introspective, less reactive, and more open to being vulnerable.

"After we did that work with little B," Blake said, "my relationship with Troy transformed. I'm aware now that I was constantly treating Troy like the villain and that those feelings were mostly driven by little B. Thanks so much for helping me with this."

Another example of a cumulative unburdening showed up with a client of mine named Janis who healed a school-aged little girl who felt unloved by her mother. I randomly checked in with Janis several months later to see how the girl was doing.

"To tell you the truth, I wasn't able to be completely honest with her at that time because I was still drinking daily back then. I was as present as I could have been, but I think she needs another round of help now that I'm sober and can be more fully present for her," Janis said.

Here, Janis was only capable of doing a small percentage of the healing due to her daily drinking. As she got sober, she became more capable of healing other layers of the little girl's pain.

TRADITIONAL UNBURDENING

Traditional unburdening is the type of healing most of us are familiar with and are taught in IFS Level 1 training. This kind of unburdening can theoretically happen all in one sitting. It can be impactful, be powerful to witness, and typically have a big effect on the quality of a client's life. Here, the client's Self is the primary healing agent, and the therapist's presence gently guides the process to completion. Often, this unburdening involves one exile carrying one wound. Or, with complex trauma, it can be one exile carrying several wounds, several exiles carrying a similar wound, exiles carrying a wound from each parent, exiles in the present connected to exiles in the past, or several different exiles carrying several different wounds.

The following graphic depicts the different types of unburdening that occur in relational trauma. They typically progress from left to right as treatment unfolds.

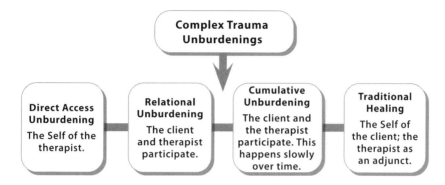

Here is a summary chart that represents the range of unburdenings along with the different configurations of wounds that show up in complex trauma.

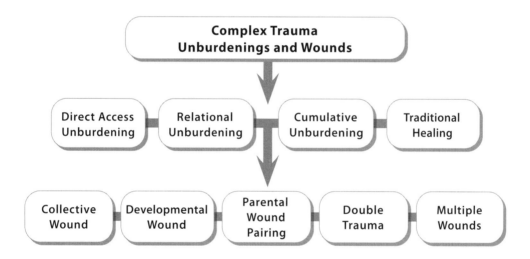

Through an IFS lens, I believe there are various ways to heal traumatic wounds and several constellations of wounds that can occur in relational violations. There are numerous ways to unload or release pain outside of the IFS framework too. People can let go of the pain they carry in a variety of different ways: through religious experiences, corrective experiences, or healing relationships; by being in nature or reading something impactful; by using medicines; and via different psychotherapy modalities.

For me, IFS is the most comprehensive treatment modality. It incorporates thoughts, feelings, physical sensations, inner wisdom, energy, relationships, and spirituality. It makes the most intuitive sense to me, it fits my personality and relational style, and it has been transformational in healing my trauma history. I'm happy to say that I have healthy and fulfilling relationships with the people in my life who have been abusive to me, I have truly forgiven them, and I believe this would not have been possible without the healing capacity of IFS.

CHAPTER 24

Associated Features of Healing

THE POST-UNBURDENING PROCESS

The post-unburdening process is one I believe we don't talk enough about in IFS. Typically, during our training, we focus on, teach, and demonstrate the steps of healing and rarely have the opportunity to show or discuss what happens after an unburdening. Dick Schwartz says it can take about three to four weeks before an exile appears to integrate back into the system. Again, we don't exactly know what's happening in the brain during this process, but I sense that it has something to do with reinforcing the newly reorganized neural network. Hopefully, with further research, we'll have more clarity and definitive answers here. I recommend that clients *briefly check in with their unburdened part every day for about three to four weeks*, as Dick Schwartz has advised. I've noticed that when I've done this with my own newly healed parts, they gently fade into the background and become part of my overall system.

There seems to be an *integration phase* that occurs after healing. It's like putting the pieces of a puzzle together in a new, organic way, and this seems to happen both internally as well as externally. There's a *new way of being in the world*—one that no longer includes being triggered, which can take some getting used to for clients. There also seems to be a process of putting the past into perspective, seeing the world differently in the present, and allowing it to unfold without needing to be in control.

To demonstrate the power of the post-unburdening process, here is a sample of a session dialogue I shared with a client named Jena:

"Jena, how is your 36-year-old part doing this week?" I asked, referring to an unburdened adult part that was thrown to the floor by Mike (her husband) after he found out that she quit her job without telling him.

"I've been checking in with her like you had asked me to—not every day but most days," she said. "She feels stronger. She is more emotionally settled and feels like she's able to let go of that memory and the fear associated with it. She no longer feels unloved. She's more confident and doesn't need to constantly keep her distance from Mike anymore."

"That's great, Jena. I'm happy for her. How's your drinking part doing—the main part that was protecting her for all these years?"

"Hmm. He says he no longer needs to take care of her, but he's not done drinking. He says there are other things in there he's needing to watch over." (As Jena demonstrates, parts can exhibit different genders.)

"Is he willing to share some of that with us now?" I asked.

"He's still protecting the little girl who feels unloved, the teen who lost her brother to AIDS, and the woman who had to deal with a drunk husband for the past 25 years. He has a lot of fighting left to do."

"Let him know that we're grateful he's willing to share all of this with us and that we're committed to helping him if he wants us to. It seems like he's protecting a lot of parts in there."

"Yes. The little girl is ground zero, and all the other parts are layered on top of her. It feels like my whole life is beginning to make sense for the first time."

After an unburdening has occurred, there's *a new relationship formed between the Self and the former exiled part*. It can take time for the exile and protective parts to trust that things are different now and that the Self will consistently show up, no longer leave, and handle things differently. In some circumstances, there's the potential for an overcorrection or backlash by protectors if the burden is not fully healed and protectors have not unloaded what they're carrying yet.

Here's a personal example of my healing a wound and how my parts were closely watching me as I navigated my world in a different way post-unburdening. I had unburdened a younger part of me that was frequently told what he felt and what he should feel. About a month later, my siblings and I were planning a surprise birthday party for my father, and they began suggesting to me what I should and shouldn't feel. I started noticing some activation within myself, but I was surprisingly not reacting in my typical fashion. This time, I spoke up from the Self and not from my parts. I asked them if they were interested in hearing what "I" was feeling; they paused for a moment, apologized, and said: "Yes, of course we would."

I knew there was no malintent from my siblings, and I was happy with how I was able to handle things differently after healing my wound. But what was even more surprising to me was how pleased my parts were that I was able to speak up. They watched me take the lead and were pleased by it. They saw that I didn't get angry, withdraw, or just "take it"; I was instead able to stay in the conversation and represent myself differently. When I checked inside and saw my parts smiling at me, I understood the importance to them of my showing up differently. I felt a sense of warmth travel throughout my whole body.

It is important to check in with all parts after an unburdening, especially protective parts. They rarely spontaneously let go of their previous role within the system, particularly when it comes to relational trauma. They frequently continue their job and need to be *reintegrated* after a healing session, which includes trusting the Self and letting go of their old role. Or they might need to *do an unburdening themselves*, based on how they feel about the job they were forced to do in the service of protection and preservation. You might hear a client's parts say: "I feel like a piece of garbage for the ways I've treated my wife when I've been drunk" or "I don't deserve anything good in my life after yelling so much at my kids and coworkers."

Remember: Extreme parts know the effect they've had on others, and they often carry enormous shame for their behavior. Take the time they need to be integrated and release what they're carrying. If care isn't given to them to help them let go of their former role and unload their guilty feelings, they can undo the unburdening and return the exile to the past.

Post-Unburdening Process

- **Check in daily with the unburdened part for three to four weeks.**
- **Adjust to a new way of being in the world.**
- **Secure the relationship between the Self and former exile.**
- **Integrate protectors by helping them trust the Self and let go of their old roles.**
- **Allow for protector unburdening if necessary.**

When Burdens Return

Certain circumstances can bring back a burden, even after it's been healed. The conditions under which this might occur are as follows: (1) the story was not fully witnessed by the Self, (2) there's no client follow-up after an unburdening, (3) something traumatic happens in the client's life soon after an unburdening occurred, (4) other parts within the system are using the burden for some other purpose, (5) protectors are threatened by the healing and bring the burden back, or (6) a legacy burden is connected to the wound (Schwartz & Sweezy, 2020).

I've also seen that clients with more severe histories, who only have a small percentage of the Self present during an unburdening, can reverse the healing if parts don't see the Self as being able to handle things consistently enough in the present.

I noticed, for instance, that my client Amanda was displaying some of her old passive behaviors again. So I asked her to check in and see how her teenage part—the one we had helped six months earlier heal from a rape—was doing. After doing so, Amanda said, much to her surprise:

"I guess the girl has gone back into the past."

After further inquiry, we learned that the teenager had seen Amanda get depressed and had noticed that she wasn't standing up for herself anymore. The girl no longer felt safe and had lost faith in Amanda's Self as her depression worsened and her protective parts became more prominent.

This can be a common scenario, especially with clients who struggle with DID and don't have enough Self-energy consistently showing up in their lives. Protective parts or even exiles can decide to reverse the healing and return into the past.

The following is a list of the common reasons why a burden might return.

> - **The story is not fully witnessed.**
> - **There's no client follow-up after the unburdening.**
> - **Something traumatic happens in the client's life.**
> - **Other parts within the system are using the burden.**
> - **When protectors are threatened and bring the burden back.**
> - **A legacy burden is connected to the wound.**
> - **There's not enough Self-energy present for parts to trust.**

TRAUMA MEMORIES

We are therapists, not truth seekers. It's not our job to determine whether a trauma did or didn't occur. And, yes, it's common for clients to have parts that doubt whether or not it happened; it's also common for clients to have parts that ask our opinion. I try to steer clear of joining either side of that polarization. *Our job as IFS therapists is to help clients help their parts unload whatever they're carrying around a particular event in their lives.* We're not there to determine whether or not it happened as they remembered it. We stay with their experience without judgment or opinion and help them release the feelings, beliefs, and physical sensations around it. The *perception* of parts can have a powerful impact on their lives, and we can help them with that.

Anyone who works with couples knows the impact of perception. Often, one partner will have an entirely different view of what happened during an argument than the other partner, and each of their perspectives will have a huge impact on the relationship.

Again, we cannot and should not confirm or reject the accuracy of the trauma memories without definitive proof. But we can help parts unload whatever feelings they carry around it without adding to, denying, or altering their autobiographical memory.

BACKLASH

Protector backlash can be harsh, brutal, and even violent at times, especially when extreme protector parts haven't given full permission to access or heal the wounds they protect. It's one of the reasons we take getting permission so seriously in IFS. Therapists can get frustrated when it is difficult to get permission and might take advantage of the moment when an exile "storms the gate" and breaks through the protective barrier in a desperate attempt to get help.

Many of us were also psychodynamically trained and always taught to "go for the affect when it shows up." However, if an exile breaks through and you proceed with an unburdening without full permission from protectors, the healing can be reversed; even worse, severe protectors can harm clients as a punishment for going to places they've not approved of. According to Dick Schwartz, some reasons for backlash include loyalty to the perpetrator, lack of protector follow-up after an unburdening, and parts' concern over feeling content or happy.

This last point—that feeling good is not always a good thing—is something that has baffled me for a long time. I've had many clients who have courageously sorted through difficult experiences over several sessions, and we've just accomplished a big piece of work together. I've secretly expected them to arrive at the next therapy session and profusely thank me for all the ways I've aided them. Instead, they've shown up and proceeded to tell me how bad things are or how horrible they have felt since our last session. My heart has dropped with frustration and disappointment.

I've now grown accustomed to clients who suffer from relational trauma and routinely have parts of them that feel unsafe or uncomfortable when things go well and they experience joy or happiness. I've learned that the good is unfamiliar and often uncomfortable for these parts and that it often means bad things are just around the corner for them.

I now appreciate these parts. I'm committed to gently helping them acclimate to a new normal, knowing that it will take them time to adjust.

FORGIVENESS, REPAIR, AND THE POWER OF HEALING

Forgiveness and repair can be tricky for many trauma survivors. Some clients say they have no interest in repairing the relationship with their perpetrator, and they permanently sever all ties. Others will stay connected in the relationship with their abuser in an ongoing way that appears to be unhealthy. And some will forgive prematurely and struggle with not getting what they had hoped for as a response.

My suggestion to all of my clients is this: *Heal the wounds first, and then see how you feel about reaching out to your perpetrator.* Once clients release the wounds that another has caused, they are freed up, they no longer carry the trauma inside themselves, and they are untethered from their perpetrator. They possess a power from within that's rooted in love and compassion. They often have a different perspective about their feelings toward the offender and what they want to say to them.

At times, all that's required is for parts to feel truly seen and heard by the Self, and no contact with the perpetrator is necessary. At other times, after the wound is healed, clients need to name it (in a non-attacking way) and to speak up for what they know to be true. The process of reclaiming power through Self-led confrontation is impactful both internally and externally. And at other times, they're able to identify the exile underneath the perpetrator and, with a feeling of compassion, can let go and forgive. Whatever clients decide to do about confrontation, forgiveness, or repair, I always feel honored to bear witness to their process, and I trust they'll do what's best for them moving forward.

THE SCIENCE BEHIND THE HEALING

I believe that memory reconsolidation, a form of transformational neuroplasticity that Bruce Ecker talks about in his book *Unlocking the Emotional Brain*, nicely dovetails with what happens during the unburdening process in IFS. First, Ecker describes what's called the *accessing sequence*, where one identifies a current symptom and brings it from implicit (unconscious) to explicit (conscious) awareness (Ecker et al., 2012). We achieve this in IFS when protective parts grant the Self permission to be with buried or suppressed memories held within the exiled or hidden parts of our client.

Ecker next talks about the *transformation sequence*. Here, one *reactivates* the target symptom and simultaneously couples it with a *mismatch* or full contradiction of the original target's experience. The reactivation allows for the synapses on the neural network to become temporarily unstable, setting the stage for the mismatch, which promotes the correcting, updating, and rewiring of the neural network in question (Ecker et al., 2012). We see this in IFS during the witnessing and do-over steps of the unburdening process, when the Self can be with, listen to, validate, and give the part what it needed, wanted, and never got. In other words, the Self provides the exile with an opposite and fully corrective experience from its prior experience.

The next aspect of the transformation sequence includes *erasure* or revising the emotional memory with new learnings, which typically happens within approximately a five-hour window of time (Ecker et al., 2012). We see this during the retrieval, unloading, invitation, and integration steps. Here, exiles are invited to enter the present day; release their thoughts, feelings, and physical sensations; and take in the new qualities they need to move forward. We also bring protectors back so they can relinquish their old roles. All of these steps are new experiences for exiles and protectors alike.

Ecker claims that memory reconsolidation is the only known form of neuroplasticity that's capable of truly eradicating emotional learning by unlocking synapses in existing emotional memory, which doesn't impair autobiographical memory. He also compares this to counteractive change, which competes with unwanted learnings by building up new preferred learnings that override and suppress the existing ones; an example of a counteractive change would be CBT (Ecker et al., 2012).

The following chart shows the association between the accessing and transformation sequences in memory reconsolidation with the IFS unburdening process steps involved.

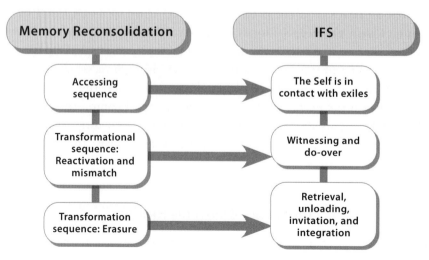

CHAPTER 25

Roadblocks to Healing

Overcoming the Barriers

Workshops and online courses that focus on treating trauma survivors are consistently some of the most popular offerings for therapists because helping clients overcome their traumatic experiences is one of the most challenging aspects of our profession. Again, extreme circumstances create extreme reactions, which creates clients who are challenging for therapists to treat.

Some common barriers consistently show up during the treatment of complex PTSD, but with proper awareness and the presence of Self-energy, you can overcome them and help your clients heal, have better connections, and access more love. This is one of the motivations for me to write this book. I have aimed to collate and share many of the experiences I've acquired over my 29 years of working with trauma survivors in the hopes that it will help you more seamlessly navigate the bumpy waters of trauma treatment with less distress and more success.

Next, we'll explore some of the common challenges IFS therapists frequently encounter during the trauma healing journey.

Psychotherapy can be moving along at a reasonable pace. Then suddenly, things start slowing down, protectors seem more entrenched, and access to Self-energy appears to wane. Here's where I look to see if an *underlying biological process* might have taken hold of my client. Is there a newly developed depression? Are they suddenly more reactive or dissociative? Did the client start drinking after a long stint of sobriety? Any of these scenarios can be a sign of an emerging biological condition in your client. It can feel like a sudden regression in the therapy, a slow-moving fog, or a heavy blanket that envelops the Self and parts. If you identify and treat this swiftly, the therapy will naturally resume; if not, sessions can continue to dredge along at a snail's pace and cause a great deal of frustration for you and your client. Remember to always ask parts if they feel that something biological is affecting them. They're usually accurate.

Some clients present with what I call *a crisis-driven system*: a series of horrible events that consistently show up with no apparent solution. These parts are more often hyperaroused in presentation and seem to thrive in chaos. I try to not get too caught up in the drama; I see these systems as largely protective, aware that the ongoing drama keeps the feelings and vulnerability away. Don't chase the crisis, as it fuels the avoidance. Over the years, I've learned to be laid back and nonreactive to these constant traumas. At times, it might even appear to my clients that I'm not very caring. But I've learned to tolerate a lot in the service of showing extreme protectors that I can handle their intensity while I continually offer them a solution to the drama: healing the wound.

We all can't be Dick Schwartz. After all, many of us have not been developing and practicing IFS for the last 35 years like he has. I'm often in awe of his extraordinary ability to put protectors at ease and to unburden exiles. But you don't have to have Dick's years of experience to be a good IFS therapist. *Know your limitations*; trauma treatment is a specialized form of therapy, and I believe that IFS is perfectly suited to help clients effectively overcome their adversity. Most importantly, *continue to work on yourself and heal your trauma*. The more unburdening I've done over the years, the less my parts show up in the office and the more I live my life guided by Self-energy. I am convinced this is precisely why the IFS model is spreading so rapidly throughout the world: It's effective, and it changes lives.

When a *therapist's parts* emerge during a client's session, boundary issues commonly arise. Most of the consultations I do are related to therapist parts. They either have parts show up that are controlling and too rigid, protecting against their own feelings of being intruded upon, or they have parts that are too soft and often cross the therapeutic line, giving to others what their internal system wanted and never got. Both extremes are common therapist parts that impede progress. Once healed, they no longer feel the need to show up in therapy.

A common and easy-to-remedy roadblock is the *lack of follow-through from session to session*. "Hello. What would you like to talk about today?" is something I usually say to identify a target part at the beginning of treatment. After that, I rarely say it again. Once we've contracted to help a target part, I want to make sure that we honor that commitment. I know that parts are watching me to see if I can be trusted and follow through with what I say. And I also know that different parts tend to show up each week to distract us from identifying and healing pain. Picking up right where you left off during the previous session will dramatically increase your chances of gaining protector permission and unburdening exiles.

Again, extreme circumstances warrant extreme responses. Many complex trauma survivors have unyielding systems that are incredibly effective at keeping the sorrow away. As a result, therapists can often feel frustrated, discouraged, and hopeless with the slow pace of progress in trauma therapy. I've found it hard at times to consistently hold the IFS frame and to stay the course with some of my more chronic clients. When things get difficult and the therapy feels stuck, it's easy to abandon the key step of trying to get permission from a resolute protector, and it's common to forget that your client has a Self, which can seem next to impossible to access sometimes. Also keep in mind that some extreme trauma protectors carry so much pain that they *need to be unburdened themselves* before they're willing to give permission to access the wound. This is a frequently overlooked roadblock but can be easily remedied by directly asking the part if it needs to unload what it's carrying before or after the exile.

It's customary for those new to the IFS model to give up on IFS and to resort back to their old therapeutic techniques due to sheer frustration. I call this the *drift factor*:

When the going gets tough and progress feels like an unrealistic pipe dream, we can lose confidence in our ability to help clients heal using IFS. As a result, we return to easier and more familiar methods, including traditional talk therapy. I know that I've certainly done this before when I can't seem to make progress in accessing my client's Self or in adequately addressing a staunch protector's fear. It's like taking a commercial break: I resort to a mostly talk therapy session and then try IFS again the next session.

Another common roadblock discussed earlier is *getting indoctrinated into the client's protective belief system*. They can wear us down over time, and we begin to believe them when they say things like: "I am much better off living alone" or "I'm too damaged to ever fully heal from the assault." These unwavering parts can be steadfast in their position, and we can gradually start to believe them. I suspect this subtle brainwashing happens more often than we're consciously aware of. This has happened to me on more than one occasion, especially with some of my longer-term chronic clients. This is why having an IFS supervision group can be enormously beneficial: having an outside perspective can help you through difficult, stuck phases in your treatment with clients.

LEGACY BURDENS

It's impossible to live in the world as we know it without carrying some form of a legacy burden. These are burdens that result from the the family we grew up in, the culture we live in, our race, our gender, our ethnicity, our sexual orientation, and other factors. *Legacy burdens often block trauma healing*, and therapists frequently don't pay attention to their presence or the impact they can have on their clients.

Part of the reason it's easy to overlook legacy burdens is that people tend to normalize their presence after living with them most of their life. It's what they've always known, and these beliefs become integrated into how they see themselves and who they think they are in the world. The good news here is that when therapists point them out, clients are usually able to identify them and release them in a variety of different ways. Dick Schwartz, Deran Young (founder of Black Therapists Rock), and Ann Sinko (a lead trainer for the IFS Institute) are among the experts in our community who speak about legacy burdens. Ann has written a chapter about legacy burdens in the book *Innovations and Elaborations in Internal Family Systems Therapy* (Sinko, 2017).

When unloading a legacy burden, it's important to help clients differentiate what percentage of the burden belongs to them (i.e., has become an internalized part of them) and what portion isn't theirs (i.e., has entered their system but belongs to someone or something outside of themselves). In either case, the legacy burden can be released. It's common for clients to be reluctant to release legacy burdens that arise within the family due to loyalty issues connected to certain relatives, especially those who are abusive. Self-energy is a great normalizer here, so addressing any parts that block access to the Self is an important step. The Self helps clients differentiate between right and wrong and gain clarity around what's important to hold on to and what they can let go of. Legacy burdens can be unloaded without the need to be witnessed, but sometimes they can carry important messages that they need to share with the client before they're willing to leave the system. It's important to help clients hear the message and realize they don't need to carry the burden's energy.

Here's a portion of a conversation I had with a client named Danielle to illustrate this point:

> "As my parts step back, I see myself as a skeleton," Danielle said. "I have consistently given myself away to the men I've been in a relationship with most of my life. It started with my first boyfriend, and now I realize I've done it with every man I've been with since—including my husband."
>
> Danielle continued: "I see myself with my mother; we're holding hands. I'm like her. We're connected in this way, giving ourselves away. This is who we are and what we do."
>
> "Danielle, are you interested in no longer carrying this burden you share with your mother?" I asked.
>
> "Most definitely. It's been a heavy weight for a long time now, for both of us."

Another client of mine, Ryan, was struggling with how hard it was for him to connect with people and with his feelings. Upon further inquiry, he also became aware that it had been challenging for him to feel empathy. Ryan's partner wondered if he was "on the spectrum," but I assured him that he wasn't. He had spent a great deal of time "figuring out" how to relate to people.

> "If you look them straight in the eyes and repeat back to them what they say to you, their faces light up and they usually respond favorably," Ryan said. "It's very effective."

Ryan's response sounded calculated and intellectual. I saw for a moment why his partner thought he might be on the spectrum. However, after further exploration, Ryan was surprised to discover a transgenerational burden the men in his family carried.

> "None of the men on my dad's side of the family could show vulnerability. This included my grandfather, my dad, me, and, unfortunately, my son and grandson too. The message was always, first and foremost, serve others and don't express yourself. Be strong, be stable, and help your fellow man. I come from a long line of preachers, and feelings weren't part of the trade; helping others was the main priority."
>
> "Believe it or not, this is something that you don't have to carry anymore," I told him. "There's a way to release this belief if you want to, Ryan."
>
> "That would be incredible," he responded.

Legacy burdens are ubiquitous; they often come from the people we grow up around, the organizations we associate with, and the culture in which we are raised. They can be subtle or dramatic in presentation. And they're often an integral part of our internal environment and typically need to be released before traumatic wounds can heal.

THE SCIENCE BEHIND LEGACY BURDENS

The IFS model has been attending to and releasing legacy burdens for quite some time, and it's exciting to finally connect them with scientific knowledge that describes the transgenerational transmission of trauma through epigenetic mechanisms.

A paper by Rachel Yehuda, one of the main researchers looking at the epigenetic transmission of PTSD, summarized much of the findings in the field and stated that there are two broad categories in offspring that can be affected by underlying epigenetic mechanisms. The first is accommodations made by offspring in response to environmental exposure early on in life; the second is the effect of preconception trauma in both parents that gets genetically transmitted to offspring through both egg and sperm. These effects can happen in utero, as well as postnatally or after birth (Yehuda & Lehrner, 2018).

More simply stated, *kids can exhibit symptoms of trauma as a result of the environment in which they grow up, as well as the genes they inherit from their parents.* A child can actually display PTSD symptoms without ever experiencing a traumatic event. DNA methylation is a proposed mechanism that is responsible for modifying gene expression and influencing the rate of genetic mutation in response to environmental challenges (Stenz et al., 2018).

Scientists believe that a better understanding of the transmission and development of PTSD will lead to future interventions and pharmacologic treatments that can reverse the consequences of early life stressors and promote greater resilience in children (Stenz et al., 2018). IFS has found a way to release these environmental and genetic effects of trauma by helping clients unload the burdens they carry from ancestors and heal the wounds they hold within their parts.

UNATTACHED BURDENS

The last roadblock to healing we'll examine is called an *unattached burden*. This is when negative energy from the environment attaches to your client's system. This is something you may not agree with or believe exists, and that is totally fine. I'm not here to impose any of my beliefs on you but to merely present what I've encountered in my practice. In my experience, people who have endured significant trauma often dissociate, or frequently leave their bodies, and can have negative energies attached to their system. These negative energies tend to block Self-energy and make it harder for clients to unburden their traumatic wounds. At first glance, unattached burdens can appear as scary, menacing, unsophisticated, and unidimensional, but their bark is much worse than their bite. They can attach to a particular part of a client, or they can attach to the client's system as a whole.

The way to determine if an unattached burden is present is to simply ask if the "part" belongs to the client or if it came from somewhere else. Believe it or not, the part will usually answer this question honestly. The process of releasing an unattached burden is similar to releasing a legacy burden; however, therapists must ensure that they, as well as their clients, embody as much Self-energy as possible because love, light, and the Self seem to be the antidote to these unattached burdens. At times, we'll even ask our clients to call in additional support from whatever help source they trust, be it God, Buddha, Jesus, Allah, or even a family member that has passed.

It's important to be brave in the face of unattached burdens, as they tend to feed off fear. As Dick often says in reference to unattached burdens: "Nothing can hurt you *internally* if you're not afraid of it." Our goal is to help disperse these energies from our client's system and to transform them into something positive. However, this requires an advanced skill that we typically teach in IFS, Trauma, and Neuroscience Level 2 training and in Level 3 training at the IFS Institute.

To comprehend the process involved with releasing unattached burdens, explore the following exchange I had with a client named David:

> "The swirling energy is back again," David said. "Every time I try to get close to the 10-year-old boy, it comes in and shuts everything down."
>
> "Can you focus on it for a few seconds and see if you can determine whether it's one of your parts doing this or if it comes from somewhere else?" I asked.
>
> "That's weird. It's not my part," David said definitively. "How do you know that?"
>
> "I didn't know it for sure. But in my experience, if we ask they'll tell us."
>
> "I'm seeing this for the first time. I took on their energy," David said.
>
> "Whose energy?"
>
> "It's a combination of my mom's and dad's energy. Her desperate sadness and the way she never let anyone get close to her. And his intense, depressed, and sexually inappropriate demeanor," David explained. "It feels like evil energy that's inside both of them."
>
> "We can release it, David," I said. "It sounds like it doesn't belong to you and that it might not belong to your parents either. Can you check that out?"
>
> "I'm getting an affirmative, that it doesn't belong to them or come from their families. This is so bizarre."
>
> "I understand that this feels a bit strange. But it's just energy, and we can release it in a way similar to how we've been able to release other painful things in your life. It's not that different," I said, trying to normalize the experience for him.

"Let's do it then. I don't want it, and I don't want them to have it either."

"I understand. We can send it away and transform it into something positive. David, bring your parents up in your mind's eye. As you focus on the swirling energy, I'm going to ask any parts of you that might be afraid of it to temporarily go into a waiting room."

"Okay, they're in the waiting room."

"Great. Now, this may sound strange, but let's have you, me, your mom, and your dad send the swirling energy as much love and light as we can. This is the best way we can help it to transform."

"I get that," David replied. After a few moments, he said: "We're all together, and there's this huge light; it's like a beacon or an enormous flashlight, and it's just shining down upon all of us. The swirling energy is slowly dissolving."

"That's beautiful, David. Just let it continue to do that until the energy is completely gone."

"This is amazing. We're all so peaceful together."

Releasing legacy-burden energy, perpetrator energy, or unattached-burden energy is similar in practice and theory. It's crucial not to react negatively toward it or to be afraid of it. Instead, stay calm, steady, and within Self-energy as you and your client send love, light, and compassion to help it transform. Asking for outside help from God, guides, angels, or ancestors sometimes helps but isn't necessary. Occasionally, we ask the energy if it has any wisdom it wants to impart before it leaves.

The following is a list of the common roadblocks associated with the treatment of complex PTSD survivors.

> - **An underlying biological condition**
> - **A crisis-driven system**
> - **Therapist limitations and unhealed trauma**
> - **Therapist parts get activated**
> - **Lack of follow-through from session to session**
> - **Extreme parts need to be unburdened first**
> - **Hard to stay on course (the drift factor)**
> - **Getting indoctrinated into the client's belief system**
> - **Legacy burdens**
> - **Unattached burdens**

CHAPTER 26

Spiritual Dimensions of Healing

GETTING OUTSIDE HELP

It's important to be mindful that our personal spiritual beliefs may or may not align with those of our clients. We need to be able and willing to move these beliefs aside if necessary, so we can be fully open and available to our clients. For example, I've had clients spontaneously mention that angels, ancestors who have passed, spirit animals, and Mother Mary appear during an unburdening session. This is often surprising to them.

When clients receive information from beyond, it's important to help them work with any skeptical parts that may come forward. Ask them: "What is the quality of the information? Does it feel more like a thought, or does it seem to come from outside themselves? Is it peaceful or disturbing?" These are questions I often ask my clients to help them differentiate between a part of them and spiritual information from beyond them, which generally has a peaceful quality and calms the system.

For instance, examine the following discourse between me and a client named Brin:

"Dr. Anderson, this is freaking me out. I'm having this weird feeling that my dog is going to die within the next few months. I'm not sure why this keeps coming up. I frequently think about it during the day at work, and sometimes I even dream about it at night. Is this some sort of premonition, or am I batshit crazy?" Brin asked.

"I'm not sure where this information is coming from either," I told her. "But in my experience, there's a qualitative difference between our thoughts, which can sometimes feel intrusive and are often rooted in fear, versus information that is sent to us from someplace outside ourselves. When it's the latter, it tends to feel soothing and has a helpful quality associated with it. Are you able to differentiate between these two regarding this information?"

"Yes," Brin replied, without hesitation. "I know what you're talking about. It's coming from beyond me. I know it, but I tend to ignore this stuff all the time. I know my dog Sammy is getting old, and I've seen signs of her failing for a while now. I can't bear the idea of losing her, and I sense that this outside force is trying to prepare me for her passing."

"Can you slow things down for a moment and just thank whoever is trying to help?"

"Yes. It feels good to have someone watching out for me like this," Brin said. "Stuff like this used to happen to my grandmother all the time too."

"I'm glad you're open to receiving help, Brin."

BEYOND THE SELF

Arjun, a client of mine who teaches high school math, was struggling with multiple medical problems, including a recent stroke, joint pain, and several environmental allergies that were triggering asthma attacks. He complained during one of our sessions that he felt like his body was falling apart and that he no longer had any control over his life. Control was something that Arjun struggled with for a long time, and he began to know it as a protective part.

"I was the only one who was capable and competent at home growing up," Arjun told me. "My mom was always popping one pill or another. And my dad's depression often got the best of him, making him an ineffective father and provider most of the time. It was my job, even as a kid, to be the competent one—the one in charge at home."

Arjun continued: "You keep telling me to go inside and listen to what my body's trying to tell me about all of this. But I'm having a hell of a time doing that. I feel like my body is totally out of control right now."

"Are you open to trying a little experiment, Arjun?" I asked. "What if you tried to let go for a moment and see if you could be open to trusting what's beyond you? What if you asked for help, trusting the goodness that's all around you, and observed what happens? Do you remember what it was like when your parts were able to take in and feel your love and support? What if you were able to try this outside of yourself?" I asked.

"I get it, Frank. My little guy liked feeling my love and support, but letting go of control and being open to what's beyond me is tough to do. Old habits die hard."

"I know, Arjun. But I wonder if you'd be open to trusting it just a little bit, right now in this moment?"

"I'm scared, but I'll try it."

After a moment of silence, I felt the energy shift in the room.

Arjun said: "It's funny, but I feel calmer right now. Something so simple has been so hard for me to do. Thank you."

The suggestion to trust, let go, and ask for help is notoriously difficult for most trauma survivors, especially when control was taken away from them at an early age. Letting go and asking for support is often challenging, but it is also relieving to parts that needed to be in control for so long.

Even though getting help from outside the Self is common and often essential in the treatment of trauma, very little can substitute a genuine and authentic Self-to-part relationship. Help from God, guides, angels, a partner, or even a therapist can be useful and incredibly impactful. I have personally found that one layer of healing often occurs with the help from outside support and, later, another layer happens between my Self and parts. Having access to what's within and what's beyond is the best of both worlds and can have a huge impact on healing the distress caused by trauma.

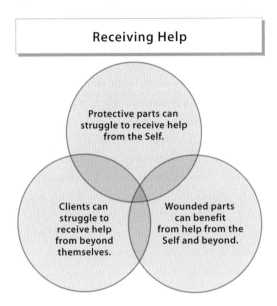

PERSONAL VIEW ON TRAUMA, LOVE, AND CONNECTION

I believe we are born into this world to have a richly rewarding human experience, learn life lessons, and experience love, creativity, and connection. I also believe that we all encounter various degrees of trauma and hardship throughout our lives that disconnect us from our Self. When we view trauma as our teacher, we address it, heal it, learn from it, and undergo growth and transformation at the soul level. I can personally say that my trauma has been a gift to me. The pain and adversity I've gone through, processed, and healed from has shaped me, taught me, helped me grow, and provided me with a rewarding career. It has helped me write this book, which hopefully will benefit countless others in overcoming their difficult life experiences.

Some of our lessons may be the result of interactions we have with people in our current life, and I believe some may show up through past life experiences. We all have been given free will and, therefore, have a choice as to how we handle our adversities. We can take advantage of them, we can bury them, or we can relive them in an attempt to repair them. I believe that adversity is an opportunity to learn and grow, and when we choose to do so, it allows us to become more aligned with our truth and more connected to our source, which I trust is within us, around us, and infused with love and goodness.

I also believe that when we're connected to our core and aligned with our source, we can tap into the love and creative energy that's readily available to us. Creativity is an essential life force, which I believe is at the intersection between our soul and our source. When you're in a creative flow, it feels effortless, expansive, and magical, and you're able to produce wondrous things. We frequently see and experience this when we personally connect with various forms of art, such as music, movies, paintings, plays, and photography. Creativity can move us, make us feel something, and touch us deeply on an individual as well as a global level. It can change the world.

I feel that we're connected to an all-knowing and loving presence within us, which IFS refers to as Self-energy. I further maintain that when we're born, we simultaneously experience a separation and loss from this source energy. We live life with a deep yearning and desire to connect with that divine energy; therefore, we seek out love and connection here on Earth through our various relationships. I am convinced that our desire for connection is an attempt to unite with the love that's inherently in each of us and ultimately in the divine. In other words, when we love and connect with another person, we are connecting with God.

I further believe that the soul shares a connection with many different lifetimes, and each time we are reborn, we've contracted to learn something new and experience a different dimension of life. For example, one life experience could involve being the victim of something horrific, another could be living a privileged life, one could involve being a perpetrator, and another could be living the life of a caretaker. To truly know what it's like to be human, we need to walk in all shoes and to fully experience all aspects of life, not from a place of hate and judgment but from one of love and acceptance.

Whether our trauma or life lessons originate from the past or the present, it blocks our connection to the Self and the love embodied by the divine. I truly believe and have personally experienced that all forms and dimensions of trauma can be healed. When that happens, we learn something valuable about life. Our soul grows. And we gain greater access to the love, light, and creativity that is within us and all around us.

Trauma blocks love, connection, and creativity; and in turn, love has the power to transcend trauma, heal us, and reconnect us to our Self, our soul, our source, and each other.

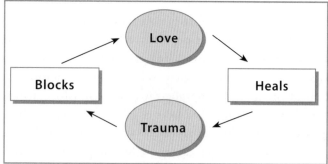

Thank you for joining me on this journey.
Love, Frank

References

For your convenience, purchasers can download and print the glossary and worksheets from www.pesi.com/Anderson

Anderson, F. G. (2013). *"Who's taking what?" Connecting neuroscience, psychopharmacology and Internal Family Systems for trauma.* In M. Sweezy & E. L. Ziskind (Eds.), *Internal Family Systems therapy: New dimensions* (pp. 107–126). Oxford: Routledge.

Anderson, F. G., Sweezy, M., & Schwartz, R. C. (2017). *Internal Family Systems skills training manual: Trauma-informed treatment for anxiety, depression, PTSD & substance abuse.* Eau Claire, WI: PESI Publishing & Media.

Bastin, C., Harrison, B., Davey, C., Moll, J., & Whittle, S. (2016). Feelings of shame, embarrassment and guilt and their neural correlates: A systematic review. *Neuroscience and Biobehavioral Reviews, 71*, 455–471.

Beck, A. T., Ward, C. H., Mendelson, M., Mock, J., & Erbaugh, J. (1961). An inventory for measuring depression. *Archives of General Psychiatry, 4,* 561–571.

Beckes, L., & Coan, J. A. (2011). Social baseline theory: The role of social proximity in emotion and economy of action. *Social and Personality Psychology Compass, 5*(12), 976–988.

Benau, K. (2019, July 1). Care sought and unmet is shaming. *The Science of Psychotherapy.* Retrieved from https://www.thescienceofpsychotherapy.com/care-sought-unmet-is-shaming/

Benjet, C., Bromet, E., Karam, E. G., Kessler, R. C., McLaughlin, K. A., Ruscio, A. M., ... Koenen, K. C. (2016). The epidemiology of traumatic event exposure worldwide: Results from the World Mental Health Survey Consortium. *Psychological Medicine, 46,* 327–343.

Böckler, A., Herrmann, L., Trautwein, F. M., Holmes, T., & Singer, T. (2017). Know thy selves: Learning to understand oneself increases the ability to understand others. *Journal of Cognitive Enhancement, 1*(2), 197–209.

Brown, B. (2012). *Daring greatly: How the courage to be vulnerable transforms the way we live, love, parent, and lead.* New York: Avery.

Buydens, S. L., Wilensky, M., & Hensley, B. J. (2014). Effects of the EMDR protocol for recent traumatic events on acute stress disorder: A case series. *Journal of EMDR Practice and Research, 8*(1), 102–112.

Cloitre, M., Courtois, C. A., Ford, J. D., Green, B. L., Alexander, P., Briere, J., ... van der Hart, O. (2012). *The ISTSS expert consensus treatment guidelines for complex PTSD in adults.* Retrieved from https://www.istss.org/ISTSS_Main/media/Documents/ISTSS-Expert-Concesnsus-Guidelines-for-Complex-PTSD-Updated-060315.pdf

Cozolino, L. (2010). *The neuroscience of psychotherapy: Healing the social brain.* New York: W. W. Norton.

Cozolino, L. (2014). *The neuroscience of human relationships: Attachment and the developing social brain.* New York: W. W. Norton.

Doidge, N. (2007). *The brain that changes itself: Stories of personal triumph from the frontiers of brain science.* New York: Penguin Books.

Ecker, B., Ticic, R., & Hulley, L. (2012). *Unlocking the emotional brain: Eliminating symptoms at their roots using memory reconsolidation.* New York: Routledge.

Ettinger, B. L. (2001). Wit(h)nessing trauma and the matrixial gaze: From phantasm to trauma, from phallic structure to matrixial sphere. *Parallax, 7*(4), 89–114.

Felitti, V. J., Anda, R. F., Nordenberg, D., Williamson, D. F., Spitz, A. M., Edwards, V., Marks, J. S. (1998). Relationship of childhood abuse and household dysfunction to many of the leading causes of death in adults: The Adverse Childhood Experiences (ACE) Study. *American Journal of Preventive Medicine, 14*(4), 245–258.

Fisher, J. (2017). *Healing the fragmented selves of trauma survivors.* New York: Routledge.

Frewen, P., & Lanius, R. (2015). *Healing the traumatized self: Consciousness, neuroscience, treatment.* New York: W. W. Norton.

Guina, J., Rossetter, S. R., DeRhodes, B. J., Nahhas, R. W., & Welton, R. S. (2015). Benzodiazepines for PTSD: A systematic review and meta-analysis. *Journal of Psychiatric Practice, 21*(4), 281–303.

Hari, J. (2015, June). *Everything you think you know about addiction is wrong* [Video]. TED Conferences. https://www.ted.com/talks/johann_hari_everything_you_think_you_know_about_addiction_is_wrong?language=en

Herbine-Blank, T., Kerpelman, D., & Sweezy, M. (2016). *Intimacy from the inside out: Courage and compassion in couple therapy.* Oxford: Routledge.

Herman, J. L. (1992). Complex PTSD: A syndrome in survivors of prolonged and repeated trauma. *Journal of Traumatic Stress, 5,* 377–391.

Hodgdon, H., Anderson, F. G., Southwell, E., Hrubec, W., & Schwartz, R. C. (2017, November). *Internal Family Systems (IFS) treatment for PTSD and comorbid conditions: A pilot study.* Poster presented at the annual meeting of International Society for Traumatic Stress Studies, Chicago, IL.

Hölzel, B., Carmody, J., Evans, K., Hoge, E., Dusek, J., Morgan, L., … Lazar, S., (2010). Stress reduction correlates with structural changes in the amygdala. *Social Cognitive and Affective Neuroscience, 5*(1), 11–17.

Hölzel, B., Carmody, J., Vangel, M., Congleton, C., Yerramsetti, S., Gard, T., & Lazar, S. (2011). Mindfulness practice leads to increases in regional brain gray matter density. *Psychiatry Research: Neuroimaging, 191*(1), 36–43.

Kabat-Zinn, J. (2003). Mindfulness-based interventions in context: Past, present, and future. *Clinical Psychology: Science and Practice, 10*(2), 144–156.

Lanius, R. A., Vermetten, E., Loewenstein, R. J., Brand, B., Schmahl, C., Bremner, J. D., & Spiegel, D. (2010). Emotion modulation in PTSD: Clinical and neurobiological evidence for a dissociative subtype. *American Journal of Psychiatry, 167*(6), 640–647.

LeDoux, J. (2015). *Anxious: Using the brain to understand and treat fear and anxiety.* New York: Penguin Books.

Lyons-Ruth, K. (2003). The two-person construction of defenses: Disorganized attachment strategies, unintegrated mental states, and hostile/helpless relational processes. *Journal of Infant, Child, and Adolescent Psychotherapy, 2,* 105–114.

Lyons-Ruth, K., & Block, D. (1996). The disturbed caregiving system: Relations among childhood trauma, maternal caregiving, and infant affect and attachment. *Infant Mental Health Journal, 17*(3), 257–275.

Maté, G. (2011). *When the body says no: Understanding the stress-disease connection.* Hoboken, NJ: John Wiley & Sons.

Multidisciplinary Association for Psychedelic Studies. (2020). *MDMA-assisted psychotherapy.* Retrieved from https://maps.org/research/mdma

National Institute on Drug Abuse. (2020, May 29). *Is there a difference between physical dependence and addiction?* Retrieved from https://www.drugabuse.gov/publications/principles-drug-addiction-treatment-research-based-guide-third-edition/frequently-asked-questions/there-difference-between-physical-dependence-addiction

Neufeld, G., & Maté, G. (2014). *Hold on to your kids: Why parents need to matter more than peers.* New York: Ballantine Books.

Oxford University Press. (n.d.). *Vulnerability.* In Oxford English Dictionary. Retrieved from http://www.oxforddictionaries.com/definition/english/vulnerability

Pelcovitz, D., van der Kolk, B., Roth, S., Mandel, F., Kaplan, S., & Resick, P. (1997). Development of a criteria set and a structured interview for disorders of extreme stress (SIDES). *Journal of Traumatic Stress, 10,* 3–16.

Porges, S. (2017). *The pocket guide to the polyvagal theory: The transformative power of feeling safe.* New York: W. W. Norton.

Rasmusson, A. M., Marx, C. E., Pineles, S. L., Locci, A., Scioli-Salter, E. R., Nillni, Y. I., ... Pinna, G. (2017). Neuroactive steroids and PTSD treatment. *Neuroscience Letters, 649,* 156–163.

Rege, S., & Graham, J. (2017, November 29). Post traumatic stress disorder (PTSD): A primer on neurobiology and management. *Psych Scene Hub.* Retrieved from https://psychscenehub.com/psychinsights/post-traumatic-stress-disorder/

Schwartz, R. C. (2013). Moving from acceptance toward transformation with Internal Family Systems therapy (IFS). *Journal of Clinical Psychology, 69*(8), 805–816.

Schwartz, R. C., & Sweezy, M. (2020). *Internal Family Systems Therapy* (2nd ed.). New York: Guilford Press.

Seppala, E. (2012, December 30). The brain's ability to look within: A secret to well-being. *The Creativity Post.* Retrieved from https://www.creativitypost.com/article/the_brains_ability_to_look_within_a_secret_to_well_being

Sherin, J. E., & Nemeroff, C. B. (2011). Post-traumatic stress disorder: The neurobiological impact of psychological trauma. *Dialogues in Clinical Neuroscience, 13*(3), 263–287.

Siegel, D. (2017). *Mind: A journey to the heart of being human.* New York: W. W. Norton.

Singer, T., & Klimecki, O. (2014). Empathy and compassion. *Current Biology, 24*(18), R875–R878.

Sinko, A. L. (2017). Legacy burdens. In M. Sweezy & E. L. Ziskind (Eds.), *Innovations and elaborations in Internal Family Systems therapy* (pp. 164–178). Oxford: Routledge.

Stenz, L., Schechter, D. S., Rusconi Serpa, S., & Paoloni-Giacobino, A. (2018). Intergenerational transmission of DNA methylation signatures associated with early life stress. *Current Genomics, 19*(8), 665–675.

Substance Abuse and Mental Health Services Administration. (2014). *Trauma-informed care in behavioral health services.* Treatment Improvement Protocol (TIP) Series 57. HHS Publication No. (SMA) 13-4801. Rockville, MD: Substance Abuse and Mental Health Services Administration.

Teicher, M. H., & Samson, J. A. (2016). Annual research review: Enduring neurobiological effects of childhood abuse and neglect. *Journal of Child Psychology and Psychiatry, 57*(3), 241–266.

van der Kolk, B. A. (2005). Developmental trauma disorder: Toward a rational diagnosis for children with complex trauma histories. *Psychiatric Annals, 35*(5), 401–408.

van der Kolk, B. A. (2014). *The body keeps the score: Brain, mind, and body in the healing of trauma.* New York: Penguin Books.

Weathers, F. W., Bovin, M. J., Lee, D. J., Sloan, D. M., Schnurr, P. P., Kaloupek, D. G., ... Marx, B. P. (2018). The Clinician-Administered PTSD Scale for DSM-5 (CAPS-5): Development and initial psychometric evaluation in military veterans. *Psychological Assessment, 30,* 383–395.

Wessely, S., & Deahl, M. (2003). Psychological debriefing is a waste of time. *British Journal of Psychiatry, 183,* 12–14.

Yehuda, R., & Lehrner, A. (2018). Intergenerational transmission of trauma effects: Putative role of epigenetic mechanisms. *World Psychiatry, 17,* 243–257.

Zukav, G. (2014). *The seat of the soul (25th anniversary ed.).* New York: Simon & Schuster.

Index